KU-656-168

Success
Assessment Papers

Verbal
Reasoning

age 10–11

Alison Primrose

Sample page

examples included in each section

paper number for quick reference

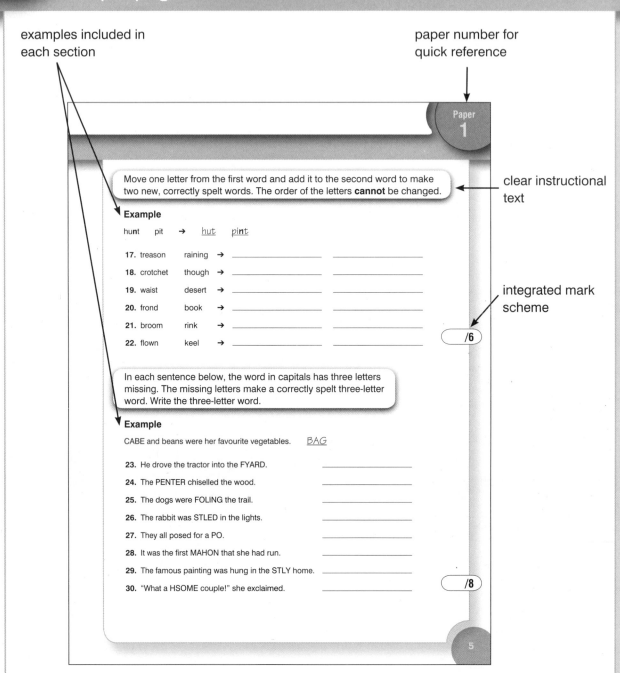

Paper 1

Move one letter from the first word and add it to the second word to make two new, correctly spelt words. The order of the letters **cannot** be changed.

← clear instructional text

Example

hunt   pit   →   hut   pint

17. treason   raining   → _____ _____
18. crotchet   though   → _____ _____
19. waist   desert   → _____ _____
20. frond   book   → _____ _____
21. broom   rink   → _____ _____
22. flown   keel   → _____ _____

/6

integrated mark scheme

In each sentence below, the word in capitals has three letters missing. The missing letters make a correctly spelt three-letter word. Write the three-letter word.

Example

CABE and beans were her favourite vegetables.   BAG

23. He drove the tractor into the FYARD. _____
24. The PENTER chiselled the wood. _____
25. The dogs were FOLING the trail. _____
26. The rabbit was STLED in the lights. _____
27. They all posed for a PO. _____
28. It was the first MAHON that she had run. _____
29. The famous painting was hung in the STLY home. _____
30. "What a HSOME couple!" she exclaimed. _____

/8

5

Contents

PAPER 1

Which two words are the most similar in meaning?
Underline one word from each set of brackets.

Example

(run, slide, swing)   (slip, skip, jump)

1. (route, explore, travel)   (location, treasure, search)
2. (wait, pressure, help)   (encourage, assist, action)
3. (teach, read, lessons)   (school, instruct, copy)
4. (dream, slumber, rest)   (solitary, bed, sleep)
5. (jump, run, crawl)   (skip, swim, sprint)
6. (heavy, burden, worry)   (parcel, load, package)
7. (wallet, cash, purse)   (money, cheque, receipt)
8. (mischief, trouble, worry) (misery, anxiety, dilemma)

/8

Choose two words, one from each set of brackets, so that the
second pair of words is completed in the same way as the first
pair. Underline the words.

Example

Solid is to (gas, lump, liquid) as ice is to (water, cube, fridge).

9. Film is to (cinema, video, leisure) as play is to (tickets, theatre, actor).
10. Skiing is to (goggles, slope, snow) as skating is to (boot, ice, speed).
11. Soap is to (water, hands, towel) as shampoo is to (curls, salon, hair).
12. Parasol is to (heat, sun, shade) as umbrella is to (rain, winter, protection).
13. Bird is to (egg, feather, aviary) as book is to (chapter, library, school).
14. Chocolate is to (cocoa, buttons, wrapper) as jelly is to (orange, party, babies).
15. Towel is to (soft, beach, dry) as shower is to (wet, cold, refreshing).
16. Black is to (grey, white, dark) as hot is to (boiling, warm, cold).

/8

Move one letter from the first word and add it to the second word to make two new, correctly spelt words. The order of the letters **cannot** be changed.

Example

hunt   pit   →   *hut*   *pint*

17. treason   raining   →   reason   trauning ✓

18. crotchet   though   →   crochet   thought

19. waist   desert   →   wait   deserts ✓

20. frond   book   →   fond   brook ✓

21. broom   rink   →   room   brink ✓

22. flown   keel   →   flow   kneel ✓

⑤ /6

In each sentence below, the word in capitals has three letters missing. The missing letters make a correctly spelt three-letter word. Write the three-letter word.

Example

CABE and beans were her favourite vegetables.   *BAG*

23. He drove the tractor into the FYARD.   arm ✓

24. The PENTER chiselled the wood.   car ✓

25. The dogs were FOLING the trail.   low ✓

26. The rabbit was STLED in the lights.   TAR / ART

27. They all posed for a PO.   hot ✓

28. It was the first MAHON that she had run.   rat ✓

29. The famous painting was hung in the STLY home.   ATE

30. "What a HSOME couple!" she exclaimed.   and ✓

⑦ /8

marathon   photo   stylish

In each of these sentences, there is a four-letter word hidden across two words. The letters are in the right order and make a correctly spelt word. Write the word.

Example

It was fis**h and** ships for supper.   <u>hand</u>

31. They had to wait for ages.   <u>rage</u> ✓

32. Each day she looked for the eggs.   <u>fort</u> ✓

33. The lambs skipped over the stile.   <u>dove</u> ✓

34. She left many years ago.   <u>Sago</u>

35. He will often visit her grave.   <u>loft</u> ✓

36. She always wore her red dress for a party.   <u>heal</u> ✓

37. He came home and went away again.   <u>mean</u> ✓

38. We must open the rusty gate.   <u>Stop</u> ✓

⑧ /8

Write these words into each grid so that they can be read across and down the grid.

Example

AYE   YET   NET   MEN   MAY   EYE

M	E	N
A	Y	E
Y	E	T

39. RED   BED   BYE   EAR   AYE   EBB

E	b	b
A	y	e
R	e	d

 ✓

40. OWE   RED   TOE   END   OWN   TOR

T	o	r
O	w	e
e	n	d

2 /2

In each group of five words below, there are three words that go together in some way. Identify the two words that **do not** belong to the group and underline them.

Example

cow   horse   <u>snake</u>   cat   <u>fly</u>

41. moon   meteor   volcano   star   earthquake

42. Summer   Autumn   June   October   Winter

43. gold   platinum   plastic   cotton   bronze

44. oak   chestnut   buttercup   ash   daisy

45. delighted   depressed   dejected   cheerful   despondent

46. chords   singer   notes   manuscript   conductor

47. paint   crayons   clay   pencil   drawing

48. rain   wind   cloud   shower   downpour

7 /8

Substitute the values for the letters and work out these equations. Give each answer as a letter.

Example

If A = 2, B = 5, C = 9, D = 14 and E = 21, what is the value of: B + C = ?   D

If A = 2, B = 5, C = 9, D = 14 and E = 21, what is the value of:

49. D × A − E + A = _C_ ✓   27

50. C + D + B ÷ A = _C × D_ ✓

51. E − B + C ÷ B = _B_ ✓

If A = 15, B = 8, C = 10, D = 30 and E = 3, what is the value of:

52. D − A + E − B = _B × C_ ✓   16

53. D ÷ E + B − C = _B_ ✓   24

53. B × E + A ÷ E − C = _e_ ✓   5

39.

4 /6

> Write the word that will complete the second pair
> of words in the same way as the first pair.

Example

PAN → NAP as TOP → ? <u>POT</u>

EVIL

55. TIME → EMIT as LIVE → ~~eliv~~ (eliv)

56. SEAT → EATS as EACH → _ache_ ✓

57. DAME → MADE as FACE → _Cafe_ ✓

58. LOSE → LOOSE as NOSE → _noose_ ✓

59. PINCH → CHIP as PATCH → _Chap_ ✓

60. VEIL → LIVE as MEAL → _lame_ ✓

5 /6

52 /60

PAPER 2

Which two words are the most similar in meaning?
Underline one word from each set of brackets.

Example

(run, <u>slide</u>, swing)   (<u>slip</u>, skip, jump)

1. (black, clouds, <u>sorrow</u>)   (old, <u>grief</u>, thunder)

2. (orchestra, music, <u>tune</u>)   (harmony, <u>melody</u>, key)

3. (<u>find</u>, hidden, seek)   (<u>search</u>, treasure, valuable)   ½

4. (landfill, <u>waste</u>, sack)   (fertiliser, bin, <u>rubbish</u>)

5. (hunt, follow, <u>rescue</u>)   (healthy, <u>retrieve</u>, antique)

6. (copse, meadow, <u>stable</u>)   (trough, <u>hedge</u>, pasture) ✗

7. (ribbon, greetings, <u>gift</u>)   (card, <u>present</u>, basket)

8. (whistle, sing, <u>wail</u>)   (speak, <u>weep</u>, hum)

/8

In each sentence below, the word in capitals has three letters
missing. The missing letters make a correctly spelt three-letter
word on their own. Write the three-letter word.

Example

CABE and beans were her favourite vegetables.   <u>BAG</u>

9. They wished them every HAPESS.   _Pin_

10. The WR was very cold!   water   _ate_

11. Tom was PLING the bulbs.   Weather   _ANT_

12. Their new AVAN was quite luxurious for holidays.   _CAR_

13. She enjoyed reading all about the latest FIONS. _____ ~~ash~~ ash

14. The children all had a part in the Christmas POMIME. _____ ant

15. They cleared the rubbish that was FING the pond. _____ ill

16. They made crumble with the RARB. _____ rhub /8

fictions

In each of these sentences, there is a four-letter word hidden across two words. The letters are in the right order and make a correctly spelt word. Write the word.

Example

It was fis**h and** chips for supper. _hand_

17. He really enjoyed his visit that day. _____ here

18. Come and see us all again. _____ mean

19. She went to the town early. _____ near

20. Find a place for me to stay! _____ form

21. They always have strawberries with cream. _____ vest

22. The fish are not rising to the bait. _____ hare

23. Can we alter the date? _____ weal

24. When is he going to address the crowd? _____ toad /8

Berfoma

Look carefully at these letter sequences. Work out the pattern to find the missing letters. Write them on the answer line.
The alphabet is here to help you.

A B C D E F G H I J K L M N O P Q R S T U V W X Y Z

Example

AB DE GH JK ? <u>MN</u>

25. AB AD AG <u>AK</u> AP

26. DC HG LK PO <u>TS</u>

27. ZX AC VT EG <u>Rp</u> IK

28. ZU YT XS <u>WR</u> VQ

29. AB DF HK <u>mq</u> SX

30. ML MO MJ MQ <u>mh</u> MS

6 /6

Rearrange the capital letters to form a correctly spelt word that will complete each sentence sensibly. Write the word on the answer line.

Example

She led the horse to the ABTESL. <u>STABLE</u>

31. The orchestra played the famous PNYSYOMH. <u>Symphony</u>

32. Sam went to RTOSPUP his home team. <u>Support</u>

33. The train arrived CULYPANTUL. <u>Puntually</u>

34. The CLEMAS carried heavy loads across the desert. <u>Camels</u>

35. It was GRUPONI with rain. <u>pouring</u>

36. The WERSPEPAN was delivered every day. <u>newspaper</u>

8 /8

37. The NOLIDSARFEG were darting around over the pond. <s>newspaper</s> <u>dragonflies</u>

38. The weather SCROFTEA warned people of the storm. <u>forecast</u>

Look carefully at the codes and work out the answers to the questions.

Example

If the code for READ is 1354, what is the code for EAR?   _351_

If the code for EAST is 7942:

39. What is the code for TEA? _279_

40. What does the code 2742 stand for? _test_

If the code for REACH is 63825:

41. What is the code for CARE? _2863_

42. What does the code 8625 stand for? _arch_

Teal tall late
The codes for LATE, TEAL and TALL are 4132, 4322 and 2341, but not in that order:

43. What is the code for TEAL? _4132_

44. What does the code 321 stand for? _ale_

45. What is the code for LET? _214_

lean Belt Ball
The codes for BELT, BALL and LEAN are 2593, 4526 and 4922, but not in that order:

46. What is the code for BENT? _4536_

47. What does the code 2935 stand for? _lane_

48. What is the code for TABLE? _69425_

_/10

Look carefully at the first two pairs of words.
Complete the third pair in the same way.

Example

part, trap   step, pets   evil, ?   _live_

49. plan, plain   man, main   pant, _Paint_

50. stream, streamer   firm, firmer   burn, _burner_

51. till, stills   lip, slips   lot, _slot_

52. camper, cap   barter, bat   canter, _Cat_

53. winter, wine   filter, file   wander, _Wane_

54. tip, tipple   lit, little   pad, _Paddle_

6/6

Choose two words, one from each set of brackets, so that the second pair of words is completed in the same way as the first pair. Underline the words.

Example

Solid is to (gas, lump, _liquid_) as ice is to (_water_, cube, fridge).

55. Hot is to (kettle, _cold_, tea) as fast is to (win, hunger, _slow_).

56. Crimson is to (paint, colour, _red_) as azure is to (haze, _blue_, sky).

57. Day is to (sun, _light_, awake) as night is to (bed, _dark_, owls).

58. Minute is to (time, hand, _hour_) as centimetre is to (mile, _metre_, ruler).

59. Bird is to (_feather_, egg, wings) as fish is to (chips, sea, _scale_).

60. Summer is to (holiday, _season_, winter) as Monday is to (work, holiday, _week_).

6/6

56/60

PAPER 3

Choose two words, one from each set of brackets, so that the second pair of words is completed in the same way as the first pair. Underline the words.

Example

Solid is to (gas, lump, liquid) as ice is to (water, cube, fridge).

1. Sweet is to (kind, pretty, sour) as happy is to (smiling, sad, friendly).

2. Cup is to (tea, spoon, saucer) as knife is to (cut, fork, cutlery).

3. Yacht is to (boat, sailing, water) as glider is to (pilot, air, runway).

4. Smile is to (laughter, face, child) as tear is to (loneliness, weeping, hanky).

5. Tall is to (tiny, lanky, short) as wide is to (plump, narrow, thin).

6. Quick is to (gently, fast, dilatory) as hot is to (tepid, scorching, melting).

7. Water is to (cold, rain, soaked) as ice to (frozen, fridge, hail).

8. Paint is to (colour, water, brush) as ink is to (writing, pen, letters).

/8

Look carefully at the codes and work out the answers to the questions.

Example

If the code for READ is 1354, what is the code for EAR?   3 5 1

If the code for CRANE is 53721:

9. What is the code for RACE? __3751__

10. What does the code 2173 stand for? __near__

tent mint mate

If the codes for MATE, MINT and TENT are 5365, 1265 and 1753, but not in that order:

11. What is the code for MATE? __1753__

12. What is the code for TIME? __5213__

13. What does the code 1263 stand for? __mine__

If the codes for BEN, TEN and BAN are QRY, UZY and URY, but not in that order:

ten Ban Ben (handwritten above)

14. What is the code for BAN? __UZY__

15. What does the code QRYQ stand for? __tent__

16. What is the code for BEAT? __urzQ__

/8

> Move one letter from the first word and add it to the second word to make two new, correctly spelt words. The order of the letters **cannot** be changed.

Example

hunt   pit   → __hut__   __pint__

S (handwritten)

17. plaice   smile   → __Place__   __Simile__

18. friend   trace   → __fried__   __traced__

19. bread   mender   → _____   _____

20. prince   crow   → _____   _____

21. stile   words   → _____   _____

22. blend   grave   → _____   _____

23. reject   galley   → _____   _____

24. panther   irate   → _____   _____

/8

> In each of these sentences, there is a four-letter word hidden across two words. The letters are in the right order and make a correctly spelt word. Write the word.

Example

It was fis**h and** chips for supper.   __hand__

25. It was proving very difficult. _____

26. It is warm over there. _____

27. There are places at the table. _____

28. Please do not rip the old flag. _____

(handwritten: fring / frend / fiend)

29. Every day our train is running late. _____

30. I will also appear on the stage. _____

31. Can I use this easel by the window? _____

32. My turn to spin the wheel. _____

/8

> Write these words into each grid so that they can be read across and down the grid.

Example

AYE   YET   NET   MEN   MAY   EYE

M	E	N
A	Y	E
Y	E	T

33. SET   OWE   HAS   PET   AWE   HOP

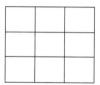

34. NEW   PEW   OWE   SAP   AWE   SON

/2

> In each group of five words below, there are three words that go together in some way. Identify the two words that **do not** belong to the group and underline them.

Example

cow   horse   <u>snake</u>   cat   <u>fly</u>

35. ballet   drama   tap   ballroom   costumes

36. ant   beetle   worm   fly   leech

37. rapid   steady   slowly   quickly   fast

38. beige   maroon   aquamarine   scarlet   crimson

39. lettuce   beetroot   carrot   cabbage   spinach

40. dollar   cheque   euro   pound   cash

41. stream brook   pond   lake   river

42. coffee   cake   tea   squash   biscuit

/8

Rearrange the capital letters to form a correctly spelt word that will complete these sentences sensibly. Write the word on the answer line.

Example

She led the horse to the ABTESL.   _STABLE_

43. She brought fresh vegetables from the MOLTATNEL. _____

44. He found the information on the TRINETEN. _____

45. Every year, the old couple visited their HDRRIGDAENNLC. _____

46. There were many SEGUFERE escaping the war zone. _____

47. They were quite breathless at the high TEDLUTIA . _____

48. He saw the RAKOSANGO jumping across the hill. _____

49. The company had a new REDTRIOC. _____

50. There was a AIRPIGMEGL to the shrine every year. _____

/8

Substitute the values for the letters and work out these equations. Give each answer as a letter.

Example

If A = 2, B = 5, C = 9, D = 14 and E = 21, what is the value of:

B + C = ?   D

If A = 5, B = 7, C = 23, D = 2 and E = 30, what is the value of:

51. A × B − E = _____

52. E + C − D − A ÷ D = _____

53. B + C + A ÷ B = _____

If A = 8, B = 2, C = 15, D = 3 and E = 20, what is the value of:

54. C + A − D = _____

55. C ÷ D + A + B = _____

56. E ÷ B − D − B + C = _____

/6

Look carefully at the first two pairs of words. Complete the third pair in the same way.

Example

part, trap   step, pets   evil, ?   live

57. frill, fill   blend, bend   trail, _____

58. repay, replay   pain, plain   payer, _____

59. have, heave   pace, peace   father, _____

60. planet, plane   comet, come   midget, _____

/4

/60

PAPER 4

Which two words are the most similar in meaning?
Underline one word from each set of brackets.

Example

(run, <u>slide</u>, swing)   (<u>slip</u>, skip, jump)

1. (<u>plenty</u>, ration, important)   (shortage, <u>enough</u>, abundance)

2. (chapter, <u>document</u>, printing)   (envelope, stamp, <u>manuscript</u>)

3. (<u>graceful</u>, jealous, golden)   (thin, <u>elegant</u>, flowery)

4. (instrument, signature, <u>message</u>)   (<u>post</u>, memo, invitation)

5. (delay, permit, <u>prohibit</u>)   (absence, <u>allow</u>, discard)

6. (hillock, puddle, stream)   (loch, brook, pipe)

7. (<u>wood</u>, mansion, avenue)   (bush, copse, <u>field</u>)

8. (predictable, <u>unusual</u>, mesmerised)   (vision, common, <u>strange</u>)

/8

Move one letter from the first word and add it to the second word to make
two new, correctly spelt words. The order of the letters **cannot** be changed.

Example

hunt   pit   →   <u>hut</u>   <u>pi**n**t</u>

9. chopper   hart   →   hopper   chart

10. saloon   muse   →   Salon   mouse

11. threads   arc   →   _____   _____

12. monkey   nave   →   _____   _____

13. feast   story   →   fast   storey

14. manager   best   →   Manage   brest

15. maize   minster   →   _____   _____

16. frigid   aster   →   _____   _____

/8

monky

In each of these sentences, there is a four-letter word hidden across two words. The letters are in the right order and make a correctly spelt word. Write the word.

Example

It was fis**h and** chips for supper. _hand_

17. Catch up with us quickly! _thus_

18. We had to climb endless steps to get there. _bend_

19. It was so warm all of the time. _mall_

20. They are always pleased to see you. _real_

21. What history do you know? _this_

22. His songs often became popular. _soft_

/6

Write these words into each grid so that they can be read across and down the grid.

Example

AYE   YET   NET   MEN   MAY   EYE

M	E	N
A	Y	E
Y	E	T

23. EVE   WAN   PEN   PEW   OVA   POP

P	O	P
e	v	e
w	a	n

24. TEN   ARE   PEN   ORE   TOT   TAP

T	a	p
o	r	e
t	e	n

/2

In each group of five words below, there are three words that go together in some way. Identify the two words that **do not** belong to the group and underline them.

Example

cow   horse   <u>snake</u>   cat   <u>fly</u>

25. scissors   knife   shears   secateurs   fork

26. mouse   keyboard   paper   message   monitor

27. bonnet   shawl   balaclava   cap   cloak

28. shout   hum   yell   scream   whistle

29. synthetic   manmade   natural   organic   artificial

30. vineyard   apples   grapes   orchard   cherries

31. alike   reject   similar   analogous   separate

32. tube   pipe   water   hose   wires

/8

Look carefully at these letter sequences. Work out the pattern to find the missing letters in each sequence. Write them on the answer line. The alphabet is here to help you.

A B C D E F G H I J K L M N O P Q R S T U V W X Y Z

Example

AB   DE   GH   JK   ?   <u>MN</u>

33. AD   CF   EH   GJ   IL   __Kn__

34. AG   MS   YE   __KQ__   WC

35. CB   FE   IH   LK   __ON__

36. ZY   XT   SR   NM   LH   _____

37. AD   EG   HK   LN   _____

38. WA   VC   UE   _____   SI

/6

21

Substitute the values for the letters and work out these equations. Give each answer as a letter.

Example

If A = 2, B = 5, C = 9, D = 14 and E = 21, what is the value of:

B + C = ? $\underline{D}$

If A = 4, B = 3, C = 12, D = 17 and E = 24, what is the value of:

39. A × B + C = ___$\underline{E}$___

40. E − D + C − B − A = ___$\underline{C}$___

41. E ÷ A − B = ___$\underline{B}$___

If V = 5, W = 8, X = 2, Y = 21 and Z = 3, what is the value of:

42. Y ÷ Z + W ÷ V = ___$\underline{Z}$___

43. Z × V + Y ÷ X − V − V = ___$\underline{X}$___

44. Z × W − Y = ___$\underline{W}$___

/6

Rearrange the capital letters to form a correctly spelt word that will complete these sentences sensibly. Write the word on the answer line.

Example

She led the horse to the ABTESL. $\underline{STABLE}$

45. The TRUNCER was strong and dangerous. _____

46. There were long ESEQUU of traffic in the town. ___~~Qui~~ Queues___

47. The NESSIOPUNS bridge across the gorge was very famous. _____

48. The meteorologist recorded the daily PARRETMEETU. _____

49. Underground they saw the most amazing SLAMGISTATE. _____

50. Each package was carefully BALEDELL. _____

51. The fresh TRICAPOS were delicious. _____

52. She looked it up in the TRYANDICIO. _____

/8

Look carefully at the first two pairs of words.
Complete the third pair in the same way.

Example

part, trap   step, pets   evil, ?   _live_

53. miles, pales   mist, past   mine, _____

54. witch, with   batch, bath   pitch, __Pith__

55. shred, shy   spring, spy   whirl, __Why__

56. past, step   kale, leek   moth, __them__

57. miser, misery   water, watery   flower, __flowery__

58. whist, list   whine, line   whisp, __lipe__

59. mount, ton   fiend, din   faint, __tan__

/7

Write these words into the grid so that they
can be read across and down the grid.

Example

STEPS   NEEDS   LAPSE   PLAIN   APPLE   POLES

P	O	L	E	S
L		A		T
A	P	P	L	E
I		S		P
N	E	E	D	S

60. HURRY   SILLY   LATER   TOTAL   WILTS   WATCH

W	a	t	C	h
i		o		u
L	a	t	e	r
t		a		r
S	i	l	l	y

/1

/60

PAPER 5

Which two words are the most similar in meaning?
Underline one word from each set of brackets.

Example

(run, <u>slide</u>, swing)   (<u>slip</u>, skip, jump)

1. (marsh, moorland, heather)   (heath, bank, park)

2. (petrol, wheels, machine)   (tower, engine, crane)

3. (funny, joke, magician)   (drama, humorous, tragedy)

4. (pacify, tired, angry)   (irrational, irate, biddable)

5. (sausages, fowl, burgers)   (poultry, beef, eggs)

6. (newspaper, verse, interview)   (prose, essay, rhyme)

7. (rake, spade, trowel)   (shovel, fork, hoe)

8. (cable, net, hammock)   (fence, wire, stirrup)

Ben
Pereira

/8

Choose two words, one from each set of brackets, so that the
second pair of words is completed in the same way as the first
pair. Underline the words.

Example

Solid is to (gas, lump, <u>liquid</u>) as ice is to (<u>water</u>, cube, fridge).

9. Litter is to (rubbish, puppies, basket) as pride is to (winner, cats, lions).

10. Fear is to (courage, fright, dark) as despair is to (worry, hope, trouble).

11. Fish is to (fingers, cakes, chips) as bread is to (sandwich, butter, loaf).

12. Gale is to (wind, storm, winter) as blizzard is to (white, mountains, snow).

13. Radio is to (listening, voices, waves) as camera is to (view, photos, eyes).

14. Tailor is to (sewing, suit, material) as barber is to (hair, scissors, cut).

15. Spring is to (rabbits, autumn, October) as summer is to (August, holidays, winter).

16. Caterpillar is to (cocoon, butterfly, eggs) as tadpole is to (frog, pond, jamjar).

/8

Look carefully at the given codes and work out the answers to the questions.

Example

If the code for READ is 1354, what is the code for EAR?   351

If the code for CHAIN is WYRPS: *PSWY*

17. What is the code for INCH? *PSWY*

18. What does the code WRS stand for? *can*

Mettall Tame

The codes for TAME, MELT and TALL are 1234, 4533 and 4512, but not in that order.

19. What does the code 4512 stand for? *Tame*

20. What is the code for MEAL? *1253*

21. What does the code 4251 stand for? *team*

dreamStart Stead

The codes for START, DREAM and STEAD are 12637, 54324 and 54631, but not in that order.

22. What is the code for DREAM? *12637*

23. What does the code 4637 stand for? *Deam*

24. What is the code for MARES? *13265*

/8

Look carefully at the first two pairs of words. Complete the third pair in the same way.

Example

part, trap   step, pets   evil, ?   *live*

25. global, lag   petal, lap   bridal, *lab*

26. train, rained   tramp, ramped   trust, *rust*

27. scout, cut   strop, top   cream, *ram*

28. flesh, self   track, cart   steps, *pets*

29. plume, plummet   line, linnet   bone, *bonnet*

/5

In each sentence below, the word in capitals has three letters missing. The missing letters make a proper three-letter word on their own. Write the three-letter word.

Example

CABE and beans were her favourite vegetables.   _BAG_

30. Sally was ill and felt MISBLE all day. _era_

31. He did some piano PRICE every day. _act_

32. The WHER was forecast fair for the camping weekend. _et_

33. She was START by the news. _led_

34. He could hardly stand because of the damage to his SE. _pin_

Wether 35. They were thrilled to be visiting the exact LOION of the film. _can_

36. The archaeologist UNTHED an old coin. _ear_

37. He quickly mended the fence using the MER. _ham_

/8

In each of these sentences, there is a four-letter word hidden across two words. The letters are in the right order and make a correctly spelt word. Write the word.

Example

Machinary

It was fis**h and** chips for supper.   _hand_

38. Everyone at home was asleep. _neat_

39. It was a lucky goal in the last minute of the match. _them_

40. They also mentioned him by name. _Some_

41. Each time, the mouse escaped under the door. _them_

42. The beach was packed with holidaymakers. _Wasp_

43. Please leave my easel over there. _love_

44. The moon shone brightly on the road ahead. _them_

45.   That winter coat is too small. _twin_

/8

Write these words into each grid so that they can be read across and down the grid.

Example

AYE   YET   NET   MEN   MAY   EYE

M	E	N
A	Y	E
Y	E	T

46. ANT   TEE   ONE   BOA   ATE   BAT

B	a	t
O	n	e
a	t	e

47. BYE   TEE   ONE   COB   CAT   ANY

C	o	b
a	n	y
t	e	e

bee

/2

Substitute the values for the letters and work out these equations. Give each answer as a letter.

Example

If A = 2, B = 5, C = 9, D = 14 and E = 21, what is the value of: B + C = ?   D

If A = 3, B = 5, C = 12, D = 18 and E = 20, what is the value of:

48. E ÷ B × A = ___ C ___

49. C + A + B = ___ E ___

If A = 22, B = 10, C = 2, D = 30 and E = 5, what is the value of:

50. D − A + C = _B_

51. E + B × C = _D_

52. D + A − C ÷ E = _6_

/5

Rearrange the capital letters to form a correctly spelt word that will complete these sentences sensibly. Write the word on the answer line.

Example

She led the horse to the ABTESL. STABLE

53. The antique table was made of YGAHMAON. _Mahatma gand_

54. Their favourite board game was STDUGRAH. _Draughts_

55. The flight was YEEDLDA. _Delayed_

56. The YIRRABL had an excellent reference section. _library_

57. They could scarcely find their way in the AZILRDZB. _blizzard_

58. She recognised him from the GOOPPARHHT. _photography_

59. He was warned not to touch the YDDLEA fungus. _deady_

60. They filmed the lion chasing the EEPLANTO. _antelope_

/8

/60

Answer booklet: Verbal Reasoning age 10–11

Paper 1
1. explore, search
2. help, assist
3. teach, instruct
4. slumber, sleep
5. run, sprint
6. burden, load
7. cash, money
8. worry, anxiety
9. cinema, theatre
10. snow, ice
11. hands, hair
12. sun, rain
13. aviary, library
14. buttons, babies
15. dry, wet
16. white, cold
17. reason   training
18. crochet   thought
19. wait   dessert/deserts
20. fond   brook
21. room   brink
22. flow   kneel
23. ARM
24. CAR
25. LOW
26. TAR (ART)
27. HOT
28. RAT
29. ATE
30. AND

There may be more than one word in some sentences:

31. rage
32. fort
33. dove
34. sago
35. loft
36. heal
37. mean
38. stop

Answers may vary:

39.
E	B	B
A	Y	E
R	E	D

40.
T	O	E
O	W	N
R	E	D

41. volcano, earthquake
42. June, October
43. plastic, cotton
44. buttercup, daisy
45. delighted, cheerful
46. singer, conductor
47. clay, drawing
48. wind, cloud
49. C
50. D
51. B
52. C
53. B
54. E
55. EVIL
56. ACHE
57. CAFE
58. NOOSE
59. CHAP
60. LAME

Paper 2
1. sorrow, grief
2. tune, melody
3. seek, search
4. waste, rubbish
5. rescue, retrieve
6. meadow, pasture
7. gift, present
8. wail, weep
9. PIN
10. ATE
11. ANT
12. CAR
13. ASH
14. ANT
15. ILL
16. HUB
17. here
18. mean
19. near
20. form
21. vest
22. hare
23. weal
24. toad
25. AK
26. TS
27. RP
28. WR
29. MQ
30. MH
31. SYMPHONY
32. SUPPORT
33. PUNCTUALLY
34. CAMELS
35. POURING
36. NEWSPAPER
37. DRAGONFLIES
38. FORECAST

39. 279
40. TEST
41. 2863
42. ARCH
43. 4132
44. ALE
45. 214
46. 4536
47. LANE
48. 69425
49. paint
50. burner
51. slots
52. cat
53. wane
54. paddle
55. cold, slow
56. red, blue
57. light, dark
58. hour, metre
59. feather, scale
60. season, week

Paper 3
1. sour, sad
2. saucer, fork
3. water, air
4. laughter, weeping
5. short, narrow
6. fast, scorching
7. rain, hail
8. brush, pen
9. 3751
10. NEAR
11. 1753
12. 5213
13. MINE
14. UZY
15. TENT
16. URZQ
17. place   simile
18. fried   trance/ fiend   tracer
19. bred   meander
20. price   crown
21. tile   swords
22. bend   gravel/ bled   graven
23. eject   gallery
24. anther   pirate
25. wasp
26. move
27. rear
28. trip
29. your
30. soap
31. seas
32. pint

Answers may vary:

33.
H	A	S
O	W	E
P	E	T

34.
S	A	P
O	W	E
N	E	W

35. drama, costumes
36. worm, leech
37. steady, slowly
38. beige, aquamarine
39. beetroot, carrot
40. cheque, cash
41. pond, lake
42. cake, biscuit
43. ALLOTMENT
44. INTERNET
45. GRANDCHILDREN
46. REFUGEES
47. ALTITUDE
48. KANGAROOS
49. DIRECTOR
50. PILGRIMAGE
51. A
52. C
53. A
54. E
55. C
56. E
57. tail
58. player
59. feather
60. midge

Paper 4
1. plenty, abundance
2. document, manuscript
3. graceful, elegant
4. message, memo
5. permit, allow
6. stream, brook
7. wood, copse
8. unusual, strange
9. hopper   chart
10. salon   mouse
11. treads   arch

12. money   knave
13. fast   storey
14. manger   beast
15. maze   minister
16. rigid   faster

There may be more than one word in some sentences:

17. thus
18. bend
19. mall
20. real
21. this
22. soft

Answers may vary:

23.
P	O	P
E	V	E
W	A	N

24.
T	O	T
A	R	E
P	E	N

25. knife, fork
26. paper, message
27. shawl, cloak
28. hum, whistle
29. natural, organic
30. vineyard, orchard
31. reject, separate
32. water, wires
33. KN
34. KQ
35. ON
36. GF
37. OR
38. TG
39. E
40. C
41. B
42. Z
43. W
44. Z
45. CURRENT
46. QUEUES
47. SUSPENSION
48. TEMPERATURE
49. STALAGMITES
50. LABELLED
51. APRICOTS
52. DICTIONARY
53. pane
54. pith
55. why
56. them
57. flowery
58. lisp
59. tan

Answers may vary:

60.
W	A	T	C	H
I		O		U
L	A	T	E	R
T		A		R
S	I	L	L	Y

Paper 5
1. moorland   heath
2. machine   engine
3. funny   humorous
4. angry   irate
5. fowl   poultry
6. verse   rhyme
7. spade   shovel
8. cable   wire
9. puppies, lions
10. courage, hope
11. chips, butter
12. wind, snow
13. voices, photos
14. material, hair
15. autumn, winter
16. butterfly, frog
17. PSWY
18. CAN
19. TAME
20. 1253
21. TEAM
22. 12637
23. TEAM
24. 73265
25. lab
26. rusted
27. ram
28. pets
29. bonnet
30. ERA
31. ACT
32. EAT
33. LED
34. PIN

35. CAT 36. EAR
37. HAM

There may be more than one word in some sentences:
38. neat 39. them
40. some 41. sees
42. wasp 43. love
44. hero 45. twin

Answers may vary:

46.

B	A	T
O	N	E
A	T	E

47.

C	O	B
A	N	Y
T	E	E

48. C 49. E
50. B 51. D
52. B 53. MAHOGANY
54. DRAUGHTS 55. DELAYED
56. LIBRARY 57. BLIZZARD
58. PHOTOGRAPH 59. DEADLY
60. ANTELOPE

Paper 6
1. haven freight
2. rouse bridge
3. miser tablet
4. evolve crater
5. tripe copes/scope
6. inch wrapper
7. fight splice
8. robe pirate
9. RAT 10. DIN
11. GIN 12. RIB
13. RUM 14. OLD
15. WIN 16. PAN
17. 5321 18. DONE
19. 2662 20. 451
21. TAPE 22. 13251

There may be more than one word in each sentence:
23. test 24. cove
25. drab 26. seat
27. nest 28. leap
29. rows 30. tall

Answers may vary:

31.

M	E	N
A	G	O
T	O	W

32.

S	E	W
A	G	O
T	O	N

33. divide, split
34. pray, mutter
35. sponge, biscuit 36. run, march
37. return, arrive 38. smooth, regular
39. sanity, shock 40. wire, chain
41. IV 42. CV
43. QU 44. PJ
45. BF 46. SQ
47. cinder 48. sting
49. hinder 50. writ
51. amp 52. spins
53. grain 54. full
55. nice 56. chopper
57. field 58. dinner
59. town 60. scent

Paper 7
1. coat, jacket 2. solitary, alone
3. couple, duo 4. change, alter
5. immediately, instantly
6. beautiful, attractive
7. valiant, heroic 8. plunge, thrust
9. gallery, museum
10. rain, sun 11. feather, fur
12. wine, cider 13. closed, exit
14. tidy, muddle
15. mistake, amendment
16. percussion, woodwind

17. older scarf
18. beach hearth
19. traced knight
20. whiter/wither tenth
21. patent claim
22. vale pound
23. raid pounce
24. miss relay
25. KIT 26. ASK
27. EAR 28. VIE
29. RID 30. DID
31. ONE 32. SEA
33. river 34. mound
35. relay 36. tuft
37. really 38. dinted
39. motor 40. plate

Answers may vary:

41.

C	A	P
O	D	E
T	O	T

42.

S	A	D
O	R	E
Y	E	W

43. NF 44. ET
45. VX 46. HE
47. KT 48. IG
49. SH 50. WB
51. MOUNTAIN 52. SCRATCHED
53. SATELLITE 54. DETECTIVE
55. PEACOCKS 56. MARATHON
57. PANTOMIME 58. AUTHOR

Answers may vary:

59.

P	R	O	U	D
A		V		U
S	T	E	M	S
T		R		T
E	N	T	R	Y

60.

R	O	C	K	S
A		A		T
P	A	N	S	Y
I		O		L
D	A	N	C	E

Paper 8
1. probe, prod
2. gleeful, jovial
3. miserable, despondent
4. ambition, aspiration
5. stroll, wander 6. push, shove
7. ask, enquire 8. swell, enlarge
9. sea, earth 10. kennel, stable
11. pie, sandwich 12. beef, mutton
13. synonyms, definitions
14. oven, fridge
15. 4356 16. BELT
17. 354 18. PINE
19. 3214 20. 3564
21. 35124 22. POTS
23. RAY 24. MEN
25. TIN 26. ACT
27. RAT 28. ATE
29. DEN 30. EEL
31. pout, grimace 32. sand, cement
33. butterfly, bee 34. cold, chilly
35. negative, harmful
36. caravan, van 37. sun, turbine
38. lose, receive 39. NO
40. VY 41. EQ
42. NP 43. KR
44. IN 45. lean
46. rim 47. trip
48. rid 49. rule
50. congregate 51. drain
52. mail 53. struts
54. wrist 55. trump
56. D 57. B

58. E 59. E
60. B

Paper 9
1. 25431 2. TASTE
3. 4632 4. PANDA
5. 215 6. DARE
7. £ >&% 8. straw, hay
9. sole, palm 10. numbers, words
11. flower, tree 12. patient, client
13. chemistry, physics
14. wrong, correct
15. stop, go
16. wader dinner
17. faction wrench
18. clave wreath
19. tent chord
20. weld painting
21. palms splatters
22. poplar proud
23. union bloom

There may be more than one word in some sentences:
24. stir 25. goal
26. echo 27. peas
28. seam 29. gout
30. arch 31. hate

Answers may vary:

32.

A	T	E
P	E	A
T	A	T

33.

C	E	P
O	V	A
N	E	W

34. shed, garage
35. variable, unpredictable
36. mature, increase
37. money, merit
38. yoghurt, grated
39. wheelbarrow, bucket
40. pilgrimage 41. hot
42. scare 43. cap
44. cry 45. tape
46. lit 47. TORRENT
48. BANQUET 49. MEADOW
50. PAVILION 51. EMERGENCY
52. MICROSCOPE
53. COLLIERY 54. TUREEN
55. gauge 56. niche
57. marry 58. stint
59. reams 60. talker

Paper 10
1. chorus, refrain
2. slip, slither
3. brush, sweep
4. cooperate, collaborate
5. exhibit, display
6. desk, bureau
7. threaten, intimidate
8. cherish, value 9. fence, hedge
10. beach, road 11. pence, cent
12. thread, arrow 13. silver, second
14. school, university
15. uncle, nephew
16. India, Japan
17. ocular jargon
18. review spender
19. sores scandal/ cores sandals
20. trice threat
21. revel forage
22. winkle frail
23. plane native
24. actor function

There may be more than one word in some sentences:
25. melt 26. chin
27. swan 28. slot
29. scar 30. eats
31. wove 32. pint

Column 1

33. eagle, chicken   34. snack, banquet
35. barometer, candle
36. detain, invite   37. slug, urchin
38. fear, battle   39. rubber, ruler
40. volcano, cave
41. dream   42. red
43. more   44. rash
45. pet   46. spotter
47. D   48. A
49. C   50. A
51. A   52. B

Answers may vary:
53. mine, dine   54. bolt, boat
55. beer, seer   56. wine, wind
57. shop, ship   58. bind, bond
59. cone, cane   60. bull, ball

Paper 11
1. imagine   pretend
2. sneak   creep
3. squash   crush
4. boundary   border
5. vivacious   lively
6. sparkling   glistening
7. SERVE   8. 42312
9. SIEVE   10. 53621
11. 1326   12. TRAIL
13. 1451435   14. REAL
15. coal, water   16. left, reverse
17. queen, countess
18. night, day
19. dusk, evening
20. voices, instruments
21. PUT   22. RAG
23. LEG   24. HER
25. LOG   26. HIS/HIM
27. ARC   28. FOR

There may be more than one word in some sentences:
29. hand   30. tank
31. meal   32. raft
33. leap   34. tour
35. sand   36. nest

Answers may vary:

37.

T	A	T
I	C	E
P	E	N

38.

P	A	Y
E	Y	E
T	E	N

39. KM   40. JL
41. NM   42. BA
43. ZJ   44. LG
45. ALPHABETICAL
46. RESERVOIR
47. FOREST
48. OSTRICH
49. DEPARTURE
50. RESTAURANT
51. cord
52. rage
53. rate
54. passive
55. single, alone
56. fierce, ferocious
57. bank, slope
58. Earth, Mars
59. quarrel, argument
60. nation, country

Paper 12
Answers may vary:
1. mint   tint
2. fine   find
3. ripe   rise
4. dame   dime
5. best   bent
6. pill   pull
7. rise, ascend
8. comedy, tragedy

Column 2

9. bottle, jar
10. nest, drey
11. red, green
12. end, conclusion
13. night   tracking
14. wave   poise
15. through   loose
16. hose   farmed/ framed
17. treble   farmer
18. breath   drink
19. these   exists
20. leased   splice/ please   sliced

Answers may vary:

21.

C	A	N
O	R	E
W	E	T

22.

B	A	N
I	C	E
D	E	W

23. desert, wilderness
24. diurnal, hibernating
25. skip, tiptoe
26. learn, follow
27. diameter, radius
28. carrots, rhubarb
29. valuable, rare
30. corrie, ridge
31. WP   32. OT
33. TI   34. JF
35. HK   36. RW
37. KO   38. BS
39. TROPICAL
40. CASSEROLE
41. CARRIAGE
42. COMPASS
43. APOLOGY
44. ANNOYED
45. FOUNTAIN
46. MARKETPLACE
47. 3465   48. 4126
49. HEAT   50. WHY
51. 1264   52. 4257
53. LINE   54. NIBBLE
55. gout   56. serve
57. pilau   58. pride
59. wines   60. coat

Paper 13
1. angel   cherub
2. flourish   brandish
3. wound   injure
4. stretch   extend
5. flee   escape
6. question   interrogate
7. famous   eminent
8. reward   recompense
9. scales, thermometer
10. knitting, sewing
11. young, youth
12. princess, duchess
13. flock, pack
14. eggs, fish
15. wood, metal
16. cheese, bone
17. crow   pendant
18. rockery   insect
19. mat   toaster
20. budge   stage
21. tread   wash
22. rouse   linger
23. dram   severe
24. staves   beret
25. LIVE   26. 41324
27. ARRIVE   28. 5614
29. 3264   30. MEET
31. 3254   32. 32615
33. MAN   34. CAN
35. ATE   36. BAR
37. HER   38. TAN
39. WIN   40. RAT

Column 3

Answers may vary:

41.

M	A	P
A	G	O
N	A	P

42.

S	A	T
I	C	E
P	E	A

43. WARDROBE
44. ENVELOPE
45. DONKEYS
46. COMPETITION
47. VINTAGE
48. CANDYFLOSS
49. OMELETTE
50. CONGRATULATIONS
51. E   52. B
53. B   54. C
55. A   56. C
57. cotton   58. ravens
59. metre   60. magic

Paper 14
1. conflict   clash
2. argument   quarrel
3. promise   pledge
4. image   picture
5. colossal   enormous
6. minute   tiny
7. segment   section
8. dream   reverie
9. ratio   mental
10. fog   cramp
11. easel   wheel
12. listen   whinge
13. hone   plump
14. potion   crook
15. latitude   sport
16. keel   broken
17. ONE   18. OLD
19. TAG   20. CUP
21. CAD   22. HAM
23. OIL   24. AND

There may be more than one word in some sentences:
25. trip   26. carp
27. tent   28. pins
29. self   30. rump
31. wasp   32. rate
33. beaver, fox
34. programme, actor
35. unusual, unique
36. mood, disposition
37. blade, stone
38. modest, diffident
39. race, advertisement
40. weevil, cockroach
41. GJ   42. GI
43. ZP   44. FE
45. JU   46. FH
47. CEREMONY
48. SERGEANT
49. SANDCASTLE
50. PANTOMIME
51. EXCITING   52. PENGUINS
53. DELICIOUS   54. DECORATED
55. 75631   56. BEER
57. 14137   58. 2351
59. SOLE   60. 43556

Paper 15
1. rash   2. tyre
3. peal   4. edge
5. vast   6. rose

Answers may vary:

7.

S	A	Y
O	W	E
N	E	T

8.

C	O	W
E	W	E
P	E	T

9. sporadic   irregular
10. consistent   reliable

11. helper — assistant
12. string — rope
13. courageous — brave
14. whisper — murmur
15. machine — turbine
16. capacious — voluminous
17. TEN   18. ARE/EAR
19. MAN   20. SPA
21. ACE   22. COP
23. RAN   24. USE
25. raid — bounce
26. have — pearl
27. patent — claim
28. back — castle
29. night — lacked
30. let — fable
31. scar — flowers
32. MG   33. FC
34. KV   35. FU
36. TY   37. ON
38. INGREDIENTS
39. FIREWORKS
40. BEAUTIFUL
41. VIOLENT
42. ABRACADABRA
43. EQUATOR
44. sound — vision
45. duke — duchess
46. cutlery — crockery
47. conductor — insulator
48. mare — ewe
49. clean — dull
50. victor — contestant
51. shiny, polish
52. pretend, purchase
53. gloves, hat
54. drink, glass
55. holly, garlic
56. concert, performance
57. 1234
58. STAR
59. 1625
60. TIARA

Paper 16

1. Answers may vary:

C	A	T
O	N	E
B	Y	E

2.

B	A	T
E	G	O
T	E	E

3. AMP   4. END
5. RAN   6. TEN
7. TOR   8. ANT
9. KIN   10. MEN
11. potent — strung
12. played — masking
13. roan — realm
14. moor — stewing
15. raking — climb
16. miss — relay

There may be more than one word in some sentences:

17. cusp   18. dale
19. gone   20. tear
21. some   22. hear
23. 5124   24. THEE
25. 56312   26. PELLET
27. 3612   28. MASH
29. 5412   30. HOSE

31. vacation, pavement
32. view, object
33. oar, paddle
34. newspaper, book
35. field, hill
36. listening, biting
37. fern, flower
38. ancient, juvenile
39. peel, tower
40. scour, hunt
41. hub, core
42. scarce, meagre
43. pattern, sequence
44. mare, donkey
45. eagle, bat
46. burger, chop
47. stove   48. keep
49. flute   50. usurp
51. miner   52. later
53. D   54. E
55. B   56. D
57. C   58. B

Answers may vary:

59.

M	A	R	S	H
A		A		O
K	I	T	E	S
E		E		E
S	I	D	E	S

60.

O	L	D	E	N
T		O		E
H	O	U	S	E
E		S		D
R	E	E	D	S

Paper 17

There may be more than one word in some sentences:

1. runt   2. twin
3. slap   4. goal
5. feet   6. solo

Answers may vary:

7.

A	S	H
Y	O	U
E	Y	E

8.

M	E	N
A	Y	E
Y	E	T

9. RIG   10. ERA
11. PIT   12. ARK
13. WIN   14. AGE
15. ally — heart
16. cider — mental
17. chip — maid
18. mender — hoarse
19. flat — veto
20. pup — blending
21. father — storey
22. aster — raft
23. TX   24. FX
25. VZ   26. LE
27. DO   28. WI
29. geology, botany
30. off, tails
31. cup, glass
32. novice, apprentice
33. saw, knife
34. limb, digit
35. polygon, polyhedron
36. end, mouth
37. please   38. town
39. coat   40. often

41. tripe   42. maroon
43. cliff, gorge
44. past, dated
45. individual, couple
46. coupons, sample
47. purse, wallet
48. poor, famous
49. sharks, eels
50. shower, glasses
51. @ # * @   52. DALE
53. > * @ > #   54. tcdue
55. GREEN   56. uctcue
57. RANG   58. E
59. E   60. C

Paper 18

Answers may vary:

1.

P	A	T
O	W	E
D	E	N

2.

T	O	P
I	D	E
N	E	T

3. specific — precise
4. rubble — debris
5. prestige — status
6. sculpture — carving
7. cape — mantle
8. dike — ditch
9. placard — hoarding
10. design — plan
11. VAN   12. CAR
13. BAN   14. ROD
15. TEE   16. ART
17. UF   18. BV
19. MT   20. BQ
21. XN   22. TP
23. FJ   24. RG
25. peal — tilting
26. cane — saucer
27. coke — hallow
28. lass — wing
29. fatten — wilt
30. wines — shelf
31. cover — planting
32. waves — leaden
33. risk   34. hero
35. tall   36. herb
37. bank   38. cone
39. climate, sun
40. prairie, plain
41. comedian, joke
42. wheelbarrow, tricycle
43. plastic, cardboard
44. trough, gate
45. accident, safety
46. emergency, crisis

Answers may vary:

47. past — pant
48. care — core
49. west — went
50. lane — lame
51. wish — wash
52. pine — pink
53. CHOCOLATE
54. SEPARATE
55. COUNTRY
56. MISSION
57. COMPASS
58. MOUNTAINS
59. KANGAROO
60. TROMBONE

PAPER 6

Move one letter from the first word and add it to the second word to make two new, correctly spelt words. The order of the words **cannot** be changed.

Example

hunt   pit   → <u>hut</u>   <u>pint</u>

1. heaven   fright   → _____   _____

2. grouse   bride   → _____   _____

3. mister   table   → _____   _____

4. revolve   cater   → _____   _____

5. stripe   cope   → _____   _____

6. winch   rapper   → _____   _____

7. flight   spice   → _____   _____

8. probe   irate   → _____   _____

/8

In each sentence below, the word in capitals has three letters missing. The missing letters make a correctly spelt three-letter word. Write the three-letter word.

Example

CABE and beans were her favourite vegetables.   <u>BAG</u>

9. The car had a SCCH along the side. _____

10. The team were FIELG really well. _____

11. The RING bell was heard across the yard. _____

12. The TERLE accident was on the front page of the paper. _____

13. They had hot buttered CPETS for tea. _____

14. She felt BER today and spoke up for them all. _____

15. The artist had painted a TRY scene. _____

16. Next to the kitchen was an old TRY where he kept the cheese. _____   /8

> Look carefully at the codes and work out the answers to the questions.

Example

If the code for READ is 1354, what is the code for EAR?   3 5 1

If the code for POND is 4621 and the code for BONE is 5623:

17. What is the code for BEND? _____

18. What does the code 1623 stand for? _____

19. What is the code for NOON? _____

If the codes for TEA, ART and APE are 531, 542 and 125, but not in that order:

20. What is the code for PAT? _____

21. What does the code 1542 stand for? _____

22. What is the code for TREAT? _____   /6

> In each of these sentences, there is a four-letter word hidden across two words. The letters are in the right order and make a correctly spelt word. Write the word.

Example

It was fis**h and** chips for supper   hand

23. Where is my favourite stew pot? _____

24. Can you hear the music over there? _____

25. The old rabbit has taken all the carrots. _____

26. The dog is eating everything! _____

27. The famous magazine started in a small way. _____

28. Your article appeared on the front page. _____

29. May I borrow some sugar? _____

30. We must all drive there now. _____

/8

Write these words into each grid so that they can be read across and down the grid.

Example

AYE   YET   NET   MEN   MAY   EYE

31. NOW   EGO   TOW   MEN   MAT   AGO

32. WON   AGO   TON   SEW   EGO   SAT

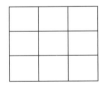

/2

In each group of five words below, there are three words that go together in some way. Identify the two words that **do not** belong to the group and underline them.

Example

cow   horse   snake   cat   fly

33. unite   divide   join   splice   split

34. weep   pray   sob   cry   mutter

35. loaf	sponge	roll	sandwich	biscuit
36. run	stroll	saunter	wander	march
37. return	go	arrive	depart	leave
38. smooth	bumpy	regular	uneven	rough
39. grief	sorrow	sanity	sadness	shock
40. rope	wire	string	cord	chain

/8

Look carefully at these letter sequences. Work out the pattern to find the missing letters. Write them on the answer line. The alphabet is here to help you.

A B C D E F G H I J K L M N O P Q R S T U V W X Y Z

Example

AB　　DE　　GH　　JK　　?　　<u>MN</u>

41. OP　　NQ　　LS　　_____　　EZ

42. GZ　　YF　　EX　　WD　　_____

43. TX　　SW　　RV　　_____　　PT

44. JI　　LJ　　JH　　NJ　　JG　　_____

45. YC　　ZD　　AE　　_____　　CG

46. BD　　AY　　FH　　WU　　JL　　_____

/8

Look carefully at the first two pairs of words. Complete the third pair in the same way.

Example

part, trap　　step, pets　　evil, ?　　<u>live</u>

47. cater, canter　　wader, wander　　cider, _____

48. strain, stain　　stroke, stoke　　string, _____

49. wand, winder   lamb, limber   hand, _____

50. night, nit .   light, lit   wright, _____

51. brash, ash   blend, end   stamp, _____

52. pot, spots   lit, slits   pin, _____

/8

Which of the following words **cannot** be made from the letters of the word written in capitals? Underline each word.

Example

STATIONERY   state   stone   <u>towns</u>   notes   train

53. ENGINEER	grin	green	reign	grain	ring
54. BEAUTIFUL	felt	table	blue	full	tube
55. MAGICIAN	nice	icing	manic	gin	main
56. HELICOPTER	police	tripe	chopper	their	three
57. WONDERFUL	fund	drone	field	rowed	flower
58. REINDEER	dine	reed	dinner	erred	rind
59. MOUNTAIN	main	moat	noun	town	mount
60. PRESENTED	step	rest	preen	scent	trees

/8

/60

PAPER 7

Which two words are the most similar in meaning? Underline one from each set of brackets.

Example

(run, <u>slide</u>, swing)   (<u>slip</u>, skip, jump)

1. (shawl, coat, jumper)   (jacket, cravat, boots)

2. (crowd, noisy, solitary)   (alone, quiet, couple)

3. (gang, couple, crowd)   (choir, quartet, duo)

4. (change, maintain, reduce)   (increase, alter, prevent)

5. (delayed, carefully, immediately)   (premature, instantly, slowly)

6. (photographic, beautiful, vivid)   (youthful, energetic, attractive)

7. (failure, soldier, valiant)   (battle, regiment, heroic)

8. (pull, plunge, draw)   (throw, thrust, carry)

/8

Choose two words, one from each set of brackets, so that the second pair of words is completed in the same way as the first pair. Underline the words.

Example

Solid is to (gas, lump, <u>liquid</u>) as ice is to (<u>water</u>, cube, fridge).

9. Painting is to (frame, gallery, artist) as artefact is to (gardens, library, museum).

10. Wellington is to (mud, country, rain) as sandal is to (hot, sun, feet).

11. Bird is to (wing, feather, nest) as dog is to (walk, lead, fur).

12. Grapes are to (vineyard, wine, juice) as apples are to (pie, chutney, cider).

13. Open is to (sign, closed, start) as entrance is to (gate, exit, admissions).

14. Neat is to (stacked, pile, tidy) as mess is to (food, muddle, mixture).

15. Error is to (bad, mistake, broken) as correction is to (amendment, strict, proof).

/8

16. Drum is to (rhythm, roll, percussion) as flute is to (music, woodwind, orchestra).

Move one letter from the first word and add it to the second word to make two new, correctly spelt words. The order of the letters **cannot** be changed.

Example

hunt   pit   →   <u>hut</u>   <u>pint</u>

17. folder   scar   → _____   _____

18. breach   heath   → _____   _____

19. tracked   night   → _____   _____

20. whither   tent   → _____   _____

21. patient   clam   → _____   _____

22. value   pond   → _____   _____

23. rapid   ounce   → _____   _____

24. amiss   rely   → _____   _____

/8

In each sentence below, the word in capitals has three letters missing. The missing letters make a correctly spelt three-letter word. Write the three-letter word.

Example

CABE and beans were her favourite vegetables.   <u>BAG</u>

25. There was a wonderful smell coming from the CHEN. _____

26. He put the precious jewels into the CET. _____

27. The dogs stretched out on the HTH rug. _____

28. They spent a long time REWING the contract. _____

29. She ran the full length of the long COROR. _____

30. It was a SPLEN concert, enjoyed by everyone. _____

31. The policeman applauded the boy for his HSTY. _____

32. They RCHED for hours trying to find the lost ball. _____

/8

Which of the following words **cannot** be made from the letters of the word written in capitals? Underline each word.

Example

STATIONERY   state   stone   <u>towns</u>   notes   train

33. RELATIVE   later   rivet   trail   river   liver

34. COMMANDER   mean   crane   dome   dream   mound

35. RAILWAY   lair   relay   wail   away   awry

36. FOUNTAIN   faint   noun   nation   tuft   font

37. BALLERINA   baler   liner   brine   aerial   really

38. NAVIGATED   given   dinted   dine   agate   dating

39. AUTOMOBILE   bloom   table   mobile   motor   tomb

40. HOSPITAL   spoil   stop   plate   pith   tails

/8

Write these words into each grid so that they can be read across and down the grid.

Example

AYE   YET   NET   MEN   MAY   EYE

M	E	N
A	Y	E
Y	E	T

41. TOT   COT   ODE   ADO   CAP   PET

42. ARE   ORE   SOD   DEW   YEW   SAY

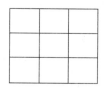

/2

Look carefully at these letter sequences. Work out the pattern to find the missing letters. Write them on the answer line. The alphabet is here to help you.

A B C D E F G H I J K L M N O P Q R S T U V W X Y Z

Example

AB   DE   GH   JK   ?   <u>MN</u>

43. ZR   JB   TL   DV   _____

44. AP   BQ   CR   DS   _____

45. MK   NP   IG   RT   EC   _____

46. ZW   TQ   NK   _____   BY

47. AB   DG   KP   VC   _____

48. YW   SU   QO   KM   _____   CE

49. MO   NL   KP   QJ   IR   _____

50. TY   UZ   VA   _____   XC

/8

Rearrange the capital letters to form a correctly spelt word that will complete each sentence sensibly. Write the word on the answer line.

Example

She led the horse to the ABTESL.   <u>STABLE</u>

51. From the NOITUNMA they could see for miles. _____

52. The kittens SCCHATRED the new furniture. _____

53. The ELILETATS beamed back pictures of other planets. _____

54. The crime scene was inspected by the EVICETTED. _____

55. The proud ECCAPKOS strutted about on the lawns. _____

56. They cheered the runners as they watched the HOAMNART. _____

57. Each Christmas, the family went to the MEANMOPTI. _____

58. The OURHAT became very popular after this new book. _____

/8

Write these words into each grid so that they can be read across and down the grid.

Example

STEPS   NEEDS   LAPSE   PLAIN   APPLE   POLES

P	O	L	E	S
L		A		T
A	P	P	L	E
I		S		P
N	E	E	D	S

59. DUSTY   ENTRY   OVERT   PASTE   STEMS   PROUD

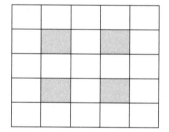

60. DANCE   STYLE   RAPID   CANON   ROCKS   PANSY

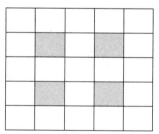

/2

/60

PAPER 8

> Which two words are the most similar in meaning?
> Underline one word from each set of brackets.

Example

(run, <u>slide</u>, swing)   (<u>slip,</u> skip, jump)

1. (probe, prance, practice)   (prod, press, precious)

2. (mystery, glory, gleeful)   (misery, jovial, smile)

3. (miserable, empty, decadent)   (miserly, despondent, deposed)

4. (amputation, actuary, ambition)   (recuperation, aspiration, restore)

5. (gallop, woodland, stroll)   (flutter, wander, crawl)

6. (push, queue, corner)   (shove, exit, alley)

7. (challenge, ask, interview)   (reply, complaint, enquire)

8. (swell, waves, manage)   (enlarge, reduce, shorten)

/8

> Choose two words, one from each set of brackets, so that the
> second pair of words is completed in the same way as the first pair.
> Underline the words.

Example

Solid is to (gas, lump, <u>liquid</u>) as ice is to (<u>water</u>, cube, fridge).

9. Fish is to (fin, sea, gills) as worm is to (wriggles, bird, earth).

10. Dog is to (bone, lead, kennel) as horse is to (rider, stable, saddle).

11. Pastry is to (apple, pie, golden) as bread is to (sandwich, bakery, loaf).

12. Cow is to (roast, beef, milk) as sheep is to (shepherd, chops, mutton).

13. Thesaurus is to (translation, synonyms, alphabet) as dictionary is to
    (lexicon, definitions, glossary).

14. Hot is to (oven, bake, sun) as cold is to (ice, winter, fridge).

/6

Look carefully at the codes and work out the answers to the questions.

Example

If the code for READ is 1354, what is the code for EAR?   *351*

If the code for STABLE is 123456:

15. What is the code for BALE? _____

16. What does the code 4652 stand for? _____

If the codes for PEA, PEN and NIP are 354, 413 and 352, but not in that order:

17. What is the code for PEN? _____

18. What does the code 3145 stand for? _____

19. What is the code for PAIN? _____

If the codes for STOP, PAST and TINT are 4124, 3564 and 6473, but not in that order:

20. What is the code for PAST? _____

21. What is the code for PAINT? _____

22. What does the code 3746 stand for? _____

/8

In each sentence below, the word in capitals has three letters missing. The missing letters make a correctly spelt three-letter word. Write the three-letter word.

Example

CABE and beans were her favourite vegetables.   *BAG*

23. The toddler loved drawing with the CONS. _____

24. The dog ran madly round in circles as if it was DETED! _____

25. It took ten hours to reach their DESATION. _____

26. It was a modern FORY producing hundreds of items every day. _____

27. He felt the VIBION from the music through the wooden floor. _____

28. He remembered to do the WRING in the greenhouse. _____

29. The security guards asked to see some form of ITITY. _____

/8

30. They sat PING potatoes ready for lunch. _____

In each group of five words below, there are three words that go together in some way. Identify the two words that **do not** belong to the group and underline them.

Example

cow   horse   <u>snake</u>   cat   <u>fly</u>

31.	wail	pout	scream	shout	grimace
32.	sand	gravel	pebbles	cement	shingle
33.	cricket	locust	butterfly	grasshopper	bee
34.	mist	cold	fog	chilly	smog
35.	nothing	zero	negative	nought	harmful
36.	liner	caravan	yacht	canoe	van
37.	sun	oil	coal	turbine	diesel
38.	maintain	lose	retain	receive	keep

/8

Look carefully at these letter sequences. Work out the pattern to find the missing letters. Write them on the answer line. The alphabet is here to help you.

A B C D E F G H I J K L M N O P Q R S T U V W X Y Z

Example

AB   DE   GH   JK   ?   <u>MN</u>

39. BC   FE   HI   LK   _____   RQ

40. PS   OP   SV   NP   _____   MP

41. AY   BW   CU   DS   _____

42. RT   QS   PR   OQ   _____

43. HU   IT   JS   _____   LQ

44. EJ   OT   YD   _____   SX

/6

Look carefully at the first two pairs of words. Complete the third pair in the same way.

Example

part, trap   step, pets   evil, ?   <u>live</u>

45. male, meal   tare, tear   lane, _____

46. ashen, she   brand, ran   grime, _____

47. medal, metal   plead, pleat   drip, _____

48. chick, hid   wreck, red   trick, _____

49. babble, bale   dabble, dale   rubble, _____

50. celebration, celebrate   notation, notate   congregation, _____

/6

Which of the following words **cannot** be made from the letters of the word written in capitals? Underline each word.

Example

| STATIONERY | state | stone | towns | notes | train |

51. STRANDED   sand   read   drain   trade   dared

52. MISSILE   lime   miss   slim   mile   mail

53. RESTAURANT   truant   treat   stare   trust   struts

54. WRESTLER   reset   were   slew   wrist   steer

55. MINIATURE   nature   train   manure   triune   trump

/5

Substitute the values for the letters and work out these equations. Give each answer as a letter.

Example

If $A = 2$, $B = 5$, $C = 9$, $D = 14$ and $E = 21$, what is the value of: $B + C = ?$ D

If $A = 4$, $B = 6$, $C = 16$, $D = 32$ and $E = 2$, what is the value of:

56. $A \times B + E + B =$ _____

57. $C \div E + D \div A - A =$ _____

If $A = 25$, $B = 7$, $C = 3$, $D = 40$ and $E = 6$, what is the value of:

58. $A - B \div C =$ _____

59. $B \times E - D \times C =$ _____

/5

60. $A + C \div B + C =$ _____

/60

PAPER 9

Look carefully at the codes and work out the answers to the questions.

Example

If the code for READ is 1354, what is the code for EAR?   3 5 1

If the code for RETREATS is 31531452:

1. What is the code for STARE? _____

2. What does the code 54251 stand for? _____

If the codes for MIND, DAMP and PAID are 4632, 2614 and 3154, but not in that order:

3. What is the code for DAMP? _____

4. What does the code 26546 stand for? _____

5. What is the code for PIN? _____

If the code for BREAD is £ & % > @:

6. What does the code @ > & % stand for? _____

7. What is the code for BARE? _____

/7

Choose two words, one from each set of brackets, so that the second pair of words is completed in the same way as the first pair. Underline the words.

Example

Solid is to (gas, lump, liquid) as ice is to (water, cube, fridge).

8. Wheat is to (bread, fields, straw) as grass is to (bale, hay, winter).

9. Foot is to (sock, toes, sole) as hand is to (palm, ring, knuckle).

10. Digits are to (tables, numbers, problems) as letters are to (calligraphy, post, words).

11. Stem is to (green, bud, flower) as trunk is to (branch, tree, wood).

12. Doctor is to (medicine, surgery, patient) as lawyer is to (judge, client, papers).

13. Elements are to (science, chemistry, school) as forces are to (physics, space, gravity).

14. Cross is to (sign, mark, wrong) as tick is to (insect, correct, sheep).

15. Red is to (wine, stop, danger) as green is to (grass, nature, go).

/8

> Move one letter from the first word and add it to the second word to make two new, correctly spelt words. The order of the letters **cannot** be changed.

Example

hunt   pit   →   <u>hut</u>   <u>pint</u>

16. wander   diner   →   _____   _____

17. fraction   wench   →   _____   _____

18. cleave   wrath   →   _____   _____

19. tenth   cord   →   _____   _____

20. wield   panting   →   _____   _____

21. Psalms   platters   →   _____   _____

22. popular   prod   →   _____   _____

23. bunion   loom   →   _____   _____

/8

> In each of these sentences, there is a four-letter word hidden across two words. The letters are in the right order and make a correctly spelt word. Write the word.

Example

It was fis**h and** chips for supper.   <u>hand</u>

24. Carrying the baggage was tiring. _____

25. Shall we go all round the town? _____

26. She chose peach and strawberry ice-cream. _____

27. She took the skipping rope as we left the house. _____

28. Please amend this letter today. _____

29. Camping out was such fun! _____

30. The bear chose to sleep in the tree. _____

31. It is what every one likes. _____

/8

Write these words into each grid so that they can be read across and down the grid.

Example

AYE   YET   NET   MEN   MAY   EYE

M	E	N
A	Y	E
Y	E	T

32. TAT   EAT   ATE   PEA   APT   TEA

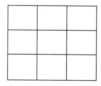

33. NEW   OVA   EVE   CEP   CON   PAW

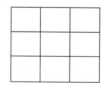

/2

In each group of five words below, there are three words that go together in some way. Identify the two words that **do not** belong to the group and underline them.

Example

cow   horse   <u>snake</u>   cat   <u>fly</u>

34. shed   garage   chalet   lodge   mansion

35. dependable   variable   unpredictable   trustworthy   reliable

36. weaken	fade	mature	lessen	increase
37. price	money	value	cost	merit
38. cottage	yoghurt	Cheddar	Brie	grated
39. spade	wheelbarrow	fork	trowel	bucket

/6

Look carefully at the first two pairs of words.
Complete the third pair in the same way.

Example

part, trap   step, pets   evil, ?   <u>live</u>

40. man, manage   post, postage   pilgrim, _____

41. western, wet   venture, vet   hostage, _____

42. tar, stare   lop, slope   car, _____

43. plain, pan   spilt, sit   cramp, _____

44. western, wry   natural, nay   concern, _____

45. match, tame   ditch, tide   patch, _____

46. count, nut   front, not   kilt, _____

/8

Rearrange the capital letters to form a correctly spelt word that will
complete these sentences sensibly. Write the word on the answer line.

Example

She led the horse to the ABTESL.   <u>STABLE</u>

47. The raging TRERNOT beneath them was quite frightening. _____

48. The ancient hall was set out for the royal TANBUQE. _____

49. The cattle grazed peacefully in the WOADEM. _____

50. The cricket team went back to the VIOLINAP for tea. _____

51. He knew how to summon help in an EEECGMNYR. _____

52. The leaf structure was observed through the COOPSIMREC. _____

53. The CRYLIELO closed when the mine shaft crumbled. _____

54. The old soup EURNTE was carefully decorated. _____

/8

Which of the following words **cannot** be made from the letters of the word written in capitals? Underline each word.

Example

STATIONERY   state   stone   <u>towns</u>   notes   train

55. PAGEANT   pent   tang   agent   gauge   page

56. CHAMPION   pinch   camp   niche   chimp   moan

57. MONARCHY   arch   roan   charm   army   marry

58. WITNESS   stint   tins   wines   newt   swine

59. MESMERISE   simmer   miser   seer   mimes   reams

60. BLANKET   belt   talker   bank   table   bleak

/6

/60

PAPER 10

Which two words are the most similar in meaning?
Underline one word from each set of brackets.

Example

(run, <u>slide</u>, swing)   (<u>slip</u>, skip, jump)

1. (voices, unison, chorus)   (prohibited, refrain, musical)

2. (sleaze, slip, slothful)   (slight, slender, slither)

3. (brush, bristle, vacuum)   (scrub, carpet, sweep)

4. (commute, argue, cooperate)   (berate, collaborate, castigate)

5. (present, conceal, exhibit)   (exposure, display, prevent)

6. (dresser, desk, chest)   (piano, bureau, mannequin)

7. (threaten, dangerous, scared)   (intimidate, horrible, pretend)

8. (possession, relation, cherish) (value, provision, vanity)

/8

Choose two words, one from each set of brackets, so that the
second pair of words is completed in the same way as the first
pair. Underline the words.

Example

Solid is to (gas, lump, <u>liquid</u>) as ice is to (<u>water</u>, cube, fridge).

9. Wire is to (line, fence, cable) as shrub is to (willow, flower, hedge).

10. Sand is to (grain, tide, beach) as tarmac is to (black, road, steamroller).

11. Pound is to (heavy, pence, coin) as dollar is to (America, money, cent).

12. Needle is to (thread, eye, sewing) as bow is to (sling, arrow, target).

13. Gold is to (precious, ring, silver) as first is to (winning, second, bronze).

14. Pupils are to (babies, school, uniform) as students are to (lecture, degree, university).

15. Aunt is to (knitting, baby, uncle) as niece is to (cousin, nephew, daughter).

16. Sari is to (Arabia, India, Tibet) as kimono is to (Japan, Mexico, Norway).

/8

> Move one letter from the first word and add it to the second word to make two new, correctly spelt words. The order of the letters **cannot** be changed.

Example

hunt   pit   →   <u>hut</u>   <u>pint</u>

17. jocular   argon   →   _____   _____

18. preview   sender   →   _____   _____

19. scores   sandal   →   _____   _____

20. thrice   treat   →   _____   _____

21. reveal   forge   →   _____   _____

22. wrinkle   fail   →   _____   _____

23. planet   naive   →   _____   _____

24. factor   unction   →   _____   _____

/8

> In each of these sentences, there is a four-letter word hidden across two words. The letters are in the right order and make a correctly spelt word. Write the word.

Example

It was fis**h and** chips for supper.   <u>hand</u>

25. The camel turned its head disdainfully. _____

26. They sat on the bench in the park. _____

27. A pig and some hens wandered around the yard. _____

28. A perfect party with balloons, lots of food and games! _____

29. The winner was carried away. _____

30. The new show was a great success. _____

31. The horse flew over the jumps! _____

32. Let's try and slip into the front row. _____

/8

> In each group of five words below, there are three words that go together in some way. Identify the two words that **do not** belong to the group and underline them.

Example

cow   horse   <u>snake</u>   cat   <u>fly</u>

33. eagle   moorhen   chicken   duck   swan

34. snack   breakfast   dinner   banquet   supper

35. clock   barometer   watch   chronometer   candle

36. detain   discard   reject   invite   decline

37. clam   slug   urchin   mussel   limpet

38. courage   fear   bravery   battle   valour

39. pen   rubber   biro   pencil   ruler

40. fountain   volcano   waterfall   rapids   cave

/8

> Look carefully at the first two pairs of words. Complete the third pair in the same way.

Example

part, trap   step, pets   evil, ?   <u>live</u>

41. crown, drown   cone, done   cream, _____

42. bottle, bet   waddle, wed   riddle, _____

43. pall, poll   warm, worm   mare, _____

44. bunch, bush   winch, wish   ranch, _____

45. node, den   wane, new   tape, _____

/6

46. top, stopper   lip, slipper   pot, _____

Substitute the values for the letters and work out these equations. Give each answer as a letter.

Example

If A = 2, B = 5, C = 9, D = 14 and E = 21, what is the value of: B + C = ?   <u>D</u>

If A = 5, B = 7, C = 12, D = 2 and E = 22, what is the value of:

47. A + B + C − E = _____

48. E + C ÷ D − C = _____

49. E + D − C = _____

If A = 30, B = 25, C = 5, D = 2 and E = 50, what is the value of:

50. E ÷ D + C = _____

51. C × D + E − A = _____

52. E − A + C = _____

/6

Change the first word into the last word, by changing one letter at a time. Each new word formed has to be a proper word, correctly spelt.

Example

SWAN   <u>swam</u>   <u>swim</u>   SLIM

53. MIND	_____	_____	DONE
54. COLT	_____	_____	BOAR
55. BEAR	_____	_____	SEED
56. WIRE	_____	_____	WAND
57. STOP	_____	_____	WHIP
58. BIRD	_____	_____	BONE
59. DONE	_____	_____	CAPE
60. BULB	_____	_____	CALL

/8

/60

PAPER 11

Which two words are the most similar in meaning?
Underline one word from each set of brackets.

Example

(run, <u>slide</u>, swing)   (<u>slip</u>, skip, jump)

1. (concerto, imagine, pressed)   (pretend, drama, reality)

2. (snare, sneak, draughty)   (creeper, creep, coerce)

3. (orange, squash, heat)   (crush, summer, shade)

4. (country, rules, boundary)   (president, border, collie)

5. (rascal, vivacious, comical)   (quiet, comatose, lively)

6. (icicle, sunlight, sparkling)   (blinding, glistening, melting)

/6

Look carefully at the codes and work out the answers to the questions.

Example

If the code for READ is 1354, what is the code for EAR?   3 5 1

If the code for SERVICE is 1234652:

7. What does the code 12342 stand for? _____

8. What is the code for VERSE? _____

9. What does the code 16242 stand for? _____

10. What is the code for CRIES? _____

The codes for TALL, TIRE, and RAIL are 5214, 5366 and 1326, but not in that order:

11. What is the code for RAIL? _____

12. What does the code 51326 stand for? _____

13. What is the code for RETREAT? _____

14. What does the code 1436 stand for? _____

/8

Choose two words, one from each set of brackets, so that the second pair of words is completed in the same way as the first pair. Underline the words.

Example

Solid is to (gas, lump, <u>liquid</u>) as ice is to (<u>water</u>, cube, fridge).

15. Mine is to (shaft, coal, dark) as well is to (water, bucket, wet).

16. Right is to (turn, correct, left) as forward is to (straight, reverse, ahead).

17. King is to (crown, queen, monarch) as count is to (countess, princess, marquis).

18. Owl is to (predator, mouse, night) as lark is to (day, feather, song).

19. Dawn is to (sunrise, dusk, early) as morning is to (day, breakfast, evening).

20. Choir is to (school, voices, songs) as orchestra is to (instruments, concert, drums).

/6

In each sentence below, the word in capitals has three letters missing. The missing letters make a correctly spelt three-letter word. Write the three-letter word.

Example

CABE and beans were her favourite vegetables.   <u>BAG</u>

21. The children took turns to play games on the COMER. _____

22. The family suffered another TEDY. _____

23. The false rumours and ALATIONS were upsetting. _____

24. The climbers wore special TMAL clothing. _____

25. They were learning about reptiles in BIOY lessons. _____

26. He spoke in a very quiet WPER. _____

27. The band played a lively MH. _____

28. The orchestra gave a wonderful PERMANCE. _____

/8

In each of these sentences, there is a four-letter word hidden across two words. The letters are in the right order and make a correctly spelt word. Write the word.

Example

It was fis**h and** chips for supper.   <u>hand</u>

29. Please wash and put the things away. _____

30. This is the best ankle support you can have. _____

31. Once upon a time, all stories started thus. _____

32. A good story has to end happily ever after. _____

33. While approaching the gate, he heard the dog bark. _____

34. The swan gracefully swam past our barge. _____

35. The fields were surrounded with fences and hedges. _____

36. The porcupine stole the dog's food. _____

/8

Write these words into each grid so that they can be read across and down the grid.

Example

AYE   YET   NET   MEN   MAY   EYE

M	E	N
A	Y	E
Y	E	T

37. PEN   TEN   ACE   ICE   TIP   TAT

38. EYE   AYE   TEN   YEN   PET   PAY

/2

Look carefully at these letter sequences. Work out the pattern to find the missing letters. Write them on the answer line. The alphabet is here to help you.

A B C D E F G H I J K L M N O P Q R S T U V W X Y Z

Example

AB   DE   GH   JK   ?   <u>MN</u>

39. BD   EG   HJ   _____

40. XV   RT   PN   _____

41. ZA   VE   RI   _____   JQ

42. GH   FE   KL   DC   OP   _____

43. XL   WM   YK   VN   _____

44. ZY   XV   UR   QM   _____

/6

Rearrange the capital letters to form a correctly spelt word that will complete each sentence sensibly.

Example

She led the horse to the ABTESL.   <u>STABLE</u>

45. The books were arranged in ETALPICAHABL order. _____

46. The REERRVOSI was in a national park. _____

47. It was dark and quiet in the middle of the STROFE. _____

48. The CHOIRST is a very fast bird. _____

49. They waited for hours in the REAPTRUDE lounge. _____

50. They had a special meal in the new TARTSURENA. _____

/6

> Look carefully at the first two pairs of words.
> Complete the third pair in the same way.

Example

part, trap   step, pets   evil, ?   <u>live</u>

51. wound, word   patent, part   commend, _____

52. potage, page   cabbage, cage   rampage, _____

53. lead, dale   mean, name   tear, _____

/4

54. manic, panic   trim, trip   massive, _____

> Which two words are the most similar in meaning?
> Underline one word from each set of brackets.

Example

(<u>costly</u>, money, price)   (cash, <u>expensive</u>, valuable)

55. (worried, quiet, single)   (pensioner, alone, refugee)

56. (fierce, strong, courageous)   (tall, ferocious, coward)

57. (bank, ditch, yard)   (hedge, slope, square)

58. (comet, Earth, galaxy)   (meteor, moon, Mars)

59. (quarrel, friend, grumpy)   (argument, cousin, discussion)

60. (nation, river, ocean)   (continent, country, lake)

/8

/60

PAPER 12

Change the first word into the last word, by changing one letter at a time. Each new word formed has to be a proper word, correctly spelt.

Example

SWAN   *swam*   *swim*   SLIM

1. MINK   _____   _____   TINY

2. PINE   _____   _____   FOND

3. ROPE   _____   _____   RISK

4. DAMP   _____   _____   MIME

5. VEST   _____   _____   BEND

6. HILL   _____   _____   PULP

/6

Choose two words, one from each set of brackets, so that the second pair of words is completed in the same way as the first pair. Underline the words.

Example

Solid is to (gas, lump, <u>liquid</u>) as ice is to (<u>water</u>, cube, fridge).

7. Fall is to (trip, rise, drop) as descend is to (lift, escalator, ascend).

8. Funny is to (comedy, laugh, joke) as sad is to (accident, tragedy, drama).

9. Wine is to (grapes, cork, bottle) as jam is to (tea, jar, sandwich).

10. Bird is to (flying, twitter, nest) as squirrel is to (drey, nuts, tail).

11. Ruby is to (ring, stone, red) as emerald is to (green, grass, sparkle).

12. Beginning is to (preface, chapter, end) as introduction is to (conclusion, index, blurb).

/6

Move one letter from the first word and add it to the second word to make two new, correctly spelt words. The order of the letters **cannot** be changed.

Example

hunt   pit   →   <u>hut</u>   <u>pint</u>

13. knight   tracing   → _____   _____

14. waive   pose   → _____   _____

15. thorough   lose   → _____   _____

16. horse   famed   → _____   _____

17. tremble   farer   → _____   _____

18. breadth   rink   → _____   _____

19. theses   exits   → _____   _____

20. pleased   slice   → _____   _____   /8

Write these words into each grid so that they can be read across and down the grid.

Example

AYE   YET   NET   MEN   MAY   EYE

M	E	N
A	Y	E
Y	E	T

21. ORE   WET   NET   ARE   CAN   COW

22. DEW   NEW   ICE   ACE   BAN   BID

/2

In each group of five words below, there are three words that go together in some way. Identify the two words that **do not** belong to the group and underline them.

Example

cow   horse   <u>snake</u>   cat   <u>fly</u>

23. plantation   desert   orchard   forest   wilderness

24. dark   diurnal   nocturnal   hibernating   night

25. canter   skip   gallop   trot   tiptoe

26. teach   learn   instruct   coach   follow

27. diameter   circumference   edge   radius   perimeter

28. lettuce   carrots   cabbage   parsley   rhubarb

29. valuable   ancient   rare   old   antique

30. valley   corrie   glen   dale   ridge

/8

Look carefully at these letter sequences. Work out the pattern to find the missing letters. Write them on the answer line. The alphabet is here to help you.

A B C D E F G H I J K L M N O P Q R S T U V W X Y Z

Example

AB   DE   GH   JK   ?   <u>MN</u>

31. AH   ZJ   YL   XN   _____

32. FP   OX   WE   DK   JP   _____

33. PA   QC   RE   SG   _____

34. YU   TP   OK   _____   EA

35. DG   FI   EH   GJ   IL   _____

36. XC   VA   TY   _____   PU

37. AA   BC   DF   GJ   _____   PU

38. EV   DU   CT   _____   AR

/8

Rearrange the capital letters to form a correctly spelt word that will complete each sentence sensibly. Write the word on the answer line.

Example

She led the horse to the ABTESL.   _STABLE_

39. It was very hot and humid in the LIPCARTO rainforest. _____

40. They could smell the OSERLACES cooking in the oven. _____

41. The horse drawn RACERAGI was used on special occasions. _____

42. With a map and SCAMPSO, they found their way. _____

43. She accepted his GOOPYAL after their quarrel. _____

44. He was DONEYAN at the interruption. _____

45. The INFATUNO was a focal point in the formal garden. _____

/8

46. The EPRAKACETLM was always bustling. _____

Look carefully at the codes and work out the answers to the questions.

Example

If the code for READ is 1354, what is the code for EAR?   _351_

If the codes for THEY, WHEN and THAN are 2415, 3465 and 2467, but not in that order:

47. What is the code for WHEN? _____

48. What is the code for HATE? _____

49. What does the code 4612 stand for? _____

50. What does the code 347 stand for? _____

If the codes for BEAD, BIND and LAND are 1354, 7564 and 1264, but not in that order:

51. What is the code for BIND? _____

52. What is the code for DIAL? _____

53. What does the code 7263 stand for? _____

54. What does the code 621173 stand for? _____

/8

> Which of the following words **cannot** be made from the letters of the word written in capitals? Underline each word.

Example

STATIONERY   state   stone   <u>towns</u>   notes   train

55. COTTAGE   coat   cage   gout   tact   tote

56. UNIVERSITY   vine   serve   unity   stir   stern

57. PALATIAL   till   pall   plait   pilau   lilt

58. BEDSPREAD   bread   spear   dread   bears   pride

59. NEWSPAPER   swap   paws   panes   pawn   wines

60. COMPUTER   crop   cure   rump   coat   trump

/6

/60

PAPER 13

Which two words are the most similar in meaning?
Underline one word from each set of brackets.

Example

(run, <u>slide</u>, swing)   (<u>slip</u>, skip, jump)

1. (angel, heaven, painting)   (halo, cherub, trumpet)

2. (flourish, hold, sheath)   (flamboyant, brandish, surreptitious)

3. (bandage, wound, accident)   (injure, fatality, stretcher)

4. (stretch, coil, elastic)   (flatten, compress, extend)

5. (return, parachute, flee)   (safari, escape, journey)

6. (interesting, question, interruption)   (questionnaire, interrogate, interpret)

7. (notorious, famous, reputation)   (fanatic, promotion, eminent)

8. (reward, gold, ransom)   (reality, recompense, famous)

/8

Choose two words, one from each set of brackets, so that the second pair of words is completed in the same way as the first pair. Underline the words.

Example

Solid is to (gas, lump, <u>liquid</u>) as ice is to (<u>water</u>, cube, fridge).

9. Weight is to (kilograms, scales, lead) as temperature is to (thermometer, hot, fever).

10. Wool is to (knitting, sheep, jumpers) as cotton is to (wool, sewing, needle).

11. Old is to (antique, ancient, young) as age is to (youth, birthday, years).

12. Prince is to (fairytale, princess, royalty) as duke is to (countess, lady, duchess).

13. Sheep are to (flock, herd, pack) as wolves are to (group, pack, coven).

14. Clutch is to (hens, cars, eggs) as school is to (teachers, fish, lessons).

15. Carpenter is to (hammer, wood, nails) as blacksmith is to (horseshoe, forge, metal).

16. Mouse is to (cheese, trap, cat) as dog is to (lead, walk, bone).

/8

Move one letter from the first word and add it to the second word to make two new, correctly spelt words. The order of the letters **cannot** be changed.

Example

hunt   pit   →   hut   pint

17. crown   pedant   →   _____   _____

18. crockery   inset   →   _____   _____

19. moat   taster   →   _____   _____

20. budget   sage   →   _____   _____

21. thread   was   →   _____   _____

22. grouse   liner   →   _____   _____

23. dream   sever   →   _____   _____

24. starves   beet   →   _____   _____

/8

Look carefully at the codes and work out the answers to the questions.

Example

If the code for READ is 1354, what is the code for EAR?   351

If the code for REVIVAL is 4231365:

25. What does the code 5132 stand for? _____

26. What is the code for RIVER? _____

27. What does the code 644132 stand for? _____

28. What is the code for LAIR? _____

The codes for SENT, TIME and MINT are 4231, 5164 and 3264, but not in that order.

29. What is the code for MINT? _____

30. What does the code 3114 stand for? _____

31. What is the code for MIST? _____

32. What is the code for MINES? _____

/8

In each sentence below, the word in capitals has three letters missing. The missing letters make a correctly spelt three-letter word. Write the three-letter word.

Example

CABE and beans were her favourite vegetables.   _BAG_

33. The rich family lived in an amazing SION. _____

34. The family left the house before the HURRIE struck. _____

35. There was enough MRIAL to make a pair of curtains. _____

36. The BER cut his hair too short. _____

37. The SHEPD went everywhere with his dogs. _____

38. It took several hours for the large KER to turn around. _____

39. In the cathedral, each DOW told a story. _____

/8

40. The extinct volcano had left an enormous CER. _____

Write these words into each grid so that they can be read across and down the grid.

Example

AYE   YET   NET   MEN   MAY   EYE

M	E	N
A	Y	E
Y	E	T

41. NAP   AGA   AGO   POP   MAP   MAN

42. ICE   ACE   PEA   SAT   SIP   TEA

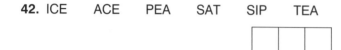

/2

> Rearrange the capital letters to form a correctly spelt word that will complete each sentence sensibly. Write the word on the answer line.

Example

She led the horse to the ABTESL.   STABLE

43. She looked in her BEADROWR to find the red dress. _____

44. Folding and putting each leaflet in an PEELOVEN took a long time! _____

45. The YEDSKON on the beach were well cared for. _____

46. They decided to enter the INEPTMOOTIC. _____

47. He inspected the GNATIVE car carefully. _____

48. They ate SANDCOYFLS as they walked around the fair. _____

49. She made an EEETOMLT with the eggs. _____

50. The wedding card sent ARTGUNICOONSALT. _____

/8

Substitute the values for the letters and work out these equations. Give each answer as a letter.

Example

If A = 2, B = 5, C = 9, D = 14 and E = 21, what is the value of: B + C = ?   <u>D</u>

If A = 16, B = 20, C = 3, D = 5 and E = 7, what is the value of:

51. B ÷ D + C = _____

52. D + E × C − A = _____

53. E − C + A = _____

If A = 5, B = 2, C = 10, D = 25 and E = 15, what is the value of:

54. E + A ÷ B = _____

55. D + C + E ÷ C = _____

56. C ÷ B + A ÷ _____

/6

Which of the following words **can** be made from the letters of the word written in capitals? Underline each word.

Example

PRESENT   scent   <u>tree</u>   tape   near   seat

57. COMPETITION   compost   impact   cotton   common   minute

58. TRANSVERSE   severe   vestry   reason   every   ravens

59. GEOMETRY   gnome   metre   energy   comet   timer

60. MAGNETIC   timing   magic   menace   entice   icing

/4

/60

PAPER 14

Which two words are the most similar in meaning?
Underline one word from each set of brackets.

Example

(run, <u>slide</u>, swing)   (<u>slip</u>, skip, jump)

1. (conflict, advance, confusion)   (clash, excursion, admonish)

2. (argument, interruption, enquiry)   (debate, apprehension, quarrel)

3. (antipathy, promise, postulate)   (disagreement, argue, pledge)

4. (expression, artistic, image)   (performance, model, picture)

5. (colossal, gregarious, conspicuous)   (splendid, enormous, extreme)

6. (daily, cyclical, minute)   (atomic, tiny, magnify)

7. (orange, partition, segment)   (petition, section, whole)

8. (apparition, goblin, dream)   (story, reverie, slumber)

/8

Move one letter from the first word and add it to the second
word to make two new, correctly spelt words. The order of the
letters **cannot** be changed.

Example

hunt   pit   →   <u>hut</u>   <u>pint</u>

9. ration   metal   →   _____   _____

10. frog   camp   →   _____   _____

11. weasel   heel   →   _____   _____

12. glisten   whine   →   _____   _____

13. phone   plum   →   _____   _____

14. portion   cook   →   _____   _____

15. platitude   sort   →   _____   _____

16. kneel   broke   →   _____   _____

/8

In each sentence below, the word in capitals has three letters missing. The missing letters make a correctly spelt three-letter word. Write the three-letter word.

Example

CABE and beans were her favourite vegetables.   BAG

17. Bees feed on nectar to make HY. _____

18. She tidied the papers and put them in the FER. _____

19. The OCONAL tiles made a wonderful pattern. _____

20. The children had to OCY themselves. _____

21. They celebrated each passing DEE. _____

22. It was a bottle of his favourite CPAGNE. _____

23. The python was CED up in the corner. _____

24. The mad man was BRISHING a stick. _____

/8

In each of these sentences, there is a four-letter word hidden across two words. The letters are in the right order and make a correctly spelt word. Write the word.

Example

It was fis**h and** chips for supper.   hand

25. Most ripe fruit will attract wasps. _____

26. They turned the car park into a market. _____

27. Please fasten the seat belt. _____

28. It was a tip inside the house. _____

29. The weasel found a way out of the cage. _____

30. The drum played loudly during the march. _____

31. The child was pushed aside. _____

32. The bear ate the fish quickly. _____

/8

In each group of five words below, there are three words that go together in some way. Identify the two words that **do not** belong to the group and underline them.

Example

cow   horse   <u>snake</u>   cat   <u>fly</u>

33. beaver   tortoise   turtle   fox   terrapin

34. production   drama   programme   performance   actor

35. common   ordinary   unusual   frequent   unique

36. tension   strain   mood   disposition   stress

37. whet   blade   sharpen   hone   stone

38. pretentious   modest   ostentatious   pompous   diffident

39. race   advertisement   challenge   confront   dispute

40. rat   weevil   cockroach   mouse   squirrel

/8

Look carefully at these letter sequences. Work out the pattern to find the missing letters. Write them on the answer line. The alphabet is here to help you.

A B C D E F G H I J K L M N O P Q R S T U V W X Y Z

Example

AB   DE   GH   JK   ?   <u>MN</u>

41. KN   JM   IL   HK   _____

42. UA   XC   AE   DG   _____   JK

43. CS   BR   AQ   _____   YO

44. ZY   BA   XW   DC   VU   _____

45. GA   HY   IW   _____   KS

46. BC   XZ   EF   BD   HI   _____

/6

Rearrange the capital letters to form a correctly spelt word that will complete each sentence sensibly. Write the word on the answer line.

Example

She led the horse to the ABTESL. ___STABLE___

47. The trumpets played a fanfare at the beginning of the MCEREYON. _____

48. The police SNTEGARE reassured the frightened lady. _____

49. There was a STSANALEDC competition on the beach. _____

50. Every year the drama group performed a IMTOPANEM. _____

51. The final match was very XITIEGCN. _____

52. The UPENSING were very comical to watch! _____

53. The cake was SLIOUCIDE. _____

54. The house was DTEECADOR for Christmas. _____

/8

Look carefully at the codes and work out the answers to the questions.

Example

If the code for READ is 1354, what is the code for EAR ? ___351___

If the code for CELEBRATE is 314125671:

55. What is the code for TRACE? _____

56. What does the code 2115 stand for? _____

57. What is the code for ELECT? _____

If the codes for TIME, MILE and SLOT are 6574, 4321 and 2351, but not in that order:

/6

58. What is the code for MILE? _____

59. What does the code 6751 stand for? _____

60. What is the code for TILLS? _____

/60

PAPER 15

In each of these sentences, there is a four-letter word hidden across two words. The letters are in the right order and make a correctly spelt word. Write the word.

Example

It was fis**h and** chips for supper. <u>hand</u>

1. The camera shots were quickly done. _____

2. Give me twenty reasons to go! _____

3. The telescope allowed us to see other planets. _____

4. The waves splashed gently round the boat. _____

5. Red hot lava stopped just short of the village. _____

6. The hero sent good wishes to all the soldiers. _____

/6

Write these words into each grid so that they can be read across and down the grid.

Example

AYE   YET   NET   MEN   MAY   EYE

M	E	N
A	Y	E
Y	E	T

7. YET   NET   OWE   SAY   AWE   SON

8. PET   OWE   EWE   WET   COW   CEP

/2

> Which two words are the most similar in meaning?
> Underline one word from each set of brackets.

Example

(run, <u>slide</u>, swing)   (<u>slip</u>, skip, jump)

9. (predictable, common, sporadic)   (frequent, even, irregular)

10. (surprising, consistent, occasional)   (fascinating, boring, reliable)

11. (carpenter, helper, apprentice)   (assistant, employer, director)

12. (stripe, dashes, string)   (link, rope, fence)

13. (boastful, bashful, courageous)   (faint, brave, wistful)

14. (silence, whisper, sing)   (mention, quieten, murmur)

15. (waterfall, power, machine)   (turbine, pipes, spray)

16. (discrete, volatile, capacious)   (capacity, voluminous, carapace)

/8

> In each sentence below, the word in capitals has three letters
> missing. The missing letters make a correctly spelt three-letter
> word on their own. Write the three-letter word.

Example

CABE and beans were her favourite vegetables.   <u>BAG</u>

17. They all LISED carefully to the instructions. _____

18. The SHERS worked each sheep quickly and deftly. _____

19. "How can I AGE without you?" _____

20. The RROW flitted around the garden. _____

21. She added the charm to her special BRLET. _____

22. They watched as the rescue HELITER arrived. _____

23. The fruit cake was full of nuts, sultanas and CURTS. _____

/8

24. The estate agent showed them many different HOS. _____

Move one letter from the first word and add it to the second word to make two new, correctly spelt words. The order of the letters cannot be changed.

Example

hunt   pit ➔ <u>hut</u>   <u>pint</u>

25. rabid   ounce   ➔   _____   _____

26. halve   pear   ➔   _____   _____

27. patient   clam   ➔   _____   _____

28. black   caste   ➔   _____   _____

29. knight   laced   ➔   _____   _____

30. left   able   ➔   _____   _____

31. scarf   lowers   ➔   _____   _____

/7

Look carefully at these letter sequences. Work out the pattern to find the missing letters. Write them on the answer line. The alphabet is here to help you.

ABCDEFGHIJKLMNOPQRSTUVWXYZ

Example

AB   DE   GH   JK   ?   <u>MN</u>

32. CQ   DP   FN   IK   _____

33. FE   FG   FD   FI   _____   FL

34. HY   IX   JW   _____   LU

35. IA   HY   GW   _____   ES

36. JK   MK   MP   TP   _____

37. WB   UE   SH   QK   _____

/6

Rearrange the capital letters to form a correctly spelt word that will complete each sentence sensibly. Write the word on the answer line.

Example

She led the horse to the ABTESL.   STABLE

38. All the IDINNTGREES for the recipe were on the shopping list. _____

39. The EWRKIROFS display was quite spectacular. _____

40. The bride looked AUFULTIBE in her flowing white dress. _____

41. The boat crashed on the rocks during the ENITOVL storm. _____

42. The magician got the children to shout BRADAACABRA as he did the trick. _____

43. The temperature increased as they sailed near to the UTOAEQR. _____

/6

Choose two words, one from each set of brackets, so that the second pair of words is completed in the same way as the first pair. Underline the words.

Example

Solid is to (gas, lump, <u>liquid</u>) as ice is to (<u>water</u>, cube, fridge).

44. Ears are to (rings, sound, muff) as eyes are to (vision, shadow, glasses).

45. Boy is to (son, child, duke) as girl is to (mother, duchess, teacher).

46. Fork is to (lunch, cutlery, food) as plate is to (crockery, china, dish).

47. Metal is to (shiny, conductor, steel) as plastic is to (bendy, cheap, insulator).

48. Stallion is to (riding, mare, stable) as ram is to (horns, ewe, lambs).

49. Dirty is to (mud, clean, wash) and shiny is to (rub, foil, dull).

50. Winner is to (loser, victor, luck) as competitor is to (individual, contestant, athlete).

/7

In each group of five words below, there are three words that go together in some way. Identify the two words that **do not** belong to the group and underline them.

Example

cow   horse   <u>snake</u>   cat   <u>fly</u>

51. shiny   bright   intelligent   polish   clever

52. mask   pretend   hide   conceal   purchase

53. boots   slippers   gloves   hat   trainers

54. squash   drink   press   crush   glass

55. holly   thyme   rosemary   garlic   mint

56. concert   cantata   performance   aria   song

/6

Look carefully at the codes and work out the answers to the questions.

Example

If the code for READ is 1354, what is the code for EAR?   <u>351</u>

The codes for TEAR, STIR and REST are 5164, 4251 and 1234, but not in that order:

57. What is the code for TEAR? _____

58. What does the code 5134 stand for? _____

59. What is the code for TIES? _____

60. What does the code 16343 stand for? _____

/4

/60

PAPER 16

Write these words into each grid so that they can be read across and down the grid.

Example

AYE   YET   NET   MEN   MAY   EYE

M	E	N
A	Y	E
Y	E	T

1. BYE   CAT   ONE   TEE   ANY   COB

2. EGO   TOE   TEE   BAT   AGE   BET

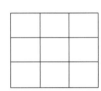

/2

In each sentence below, the word in capitals has three letters missing. The missing letters make a correctly spelt three-letter word. Write the three-letter word.

Example

CABE and beans were her favourite vegetables.   <u>BAG</u>

3. The festive HER was full of goodies. _____

4. The new neighbours were so FRILY. _____

5. They had dinner in the RESTAUT. _____

6. He used a SCIL to draw the shapes accurately. _____

7. The visitors enjoyed the HISICAL tour of the city. _____

8. In her FASY world she lived in a castle in Spain. _____

9. The TRACG device was linked to a satellite. _____

10. There was a tiny FRAGT left. _____

/8

Move one letter from the first word and add it to the second word to make two new, correctly spelt words. The order of the letters cannot be changed.

Example

hunt   pit   →   <u>hut</u>   <u>pint</u>

11. portent   stung   →   _____   _____

12. splayed   making   →   _____   _____

13. roman   real   →   _____   _____

14. motor   sewing   →   _____   _____

15. racking   limb   →   _____   _____

16. amiss   rely   →   _____   _____   /6

In each of these sentences, there is a four-letter word hidden across two words. The letters are in the right order and make a correctly spelt word. Write the word.

Example

It was fis**h and** chips for supper.   <u>hand</u>

17. The new focus papers were launched. _____

18. The giant panda led its keeper into the den. _____

19. The young ones left after six o'clock. _____

20. She left early to catch the train. _____

21. He will also mention the new book. _____

22. The artist worked quickly to finish the painting. _____   /6

Look carefully at the code and work out the answers to the questions.

Example

If the code for READ is 1354, what is the code for EAR?   <u>351</u>

If the code for TELEPHONE is 312145671:

23. What is the code for HELP? _____

24. What does the code 3511 stand for? _____

25. What is the code for HOTEL? _____

26. What does the code 412213 stand for? _____

If the codes for SHAM, HOME and SEAM are 5241, 3612 and 5341, but not in that order:

27. What is the code for HOME? _____

28. What does the code 1453 stand for? _____

29. What is the code for SAME? _____

30. What does the code 3652 stand for? _____

/8

Choose two words, one from each set of brackets, so that the second pair of words is completed in the same way as the first pair. Underline the words.

Example

Solid is to (gas, lump, underline{liquid}) as ice is to (underline{water}, cube, fridge).

31. Holiday is to (seaside, vacation, hotel) as footpath is to (road, hiking, pavement).

32. Landscape is to (view, painting, artist) as still life is to (frame, object, picture).

33. Boat is to (lifejacket, water, oar) as canoe is to (capsize, paddle, kayak).

34. Journalist is to (newspaper, television, diary) as author is to (poetry, library, book).

35. Prairie is to (cattle, field, grass) as mountain is to (brown, climbing, hill).

36. Ears are for (earrings, flapping, listening) as teeth are for (biting, brushing, dentists).

37. Frond is to (fern, weed, tree) as petal is to (stem, root, flower).

38. Old is to (grey, senile, ancient) as young is to (toddler, play, juvenile).

/8

In each group of five words below, there are three words that go together in some way. Identify the two words that **do not** belong to the group and underline them.

Example

cow   horse   underline{snake}   cat   underline{fly}

39. chime   peel   peal   ring   tower

40. scour   scrub   thorns   hunt   bush

41. shell   hub   covering   crust   core

42. abundant   scarce   profuse   copious   meagre

43. pattern   taster   sequence   sample   trial

44. lamb   kitten   mare   donkey   colt

45. butterfly   eagle   beetle   wasp   bat

46. beef   mutton   burger   pork   chop

/8

> Which of the following words **cannot** be made from the letters of the word written in capitals?

Example

STATIONERY   state   stone   <u>towns</u>   notes   train

47. FESTIVAL   feast   live   flats   stove   fives

48. PANCAKE   pack   keep   pane   neck   pace

49. WONDERFUL   drone   flute   round   flew   drown

50. SURPRISE   usurp   purrs   puss   super   spire

51. MEDALLION   medal   lion   miner   nailed   modal

52. CHOCOLATE   later   coal   cloth   halt   latch

/6

> Substitute the values for the letters and work out these equations. Give each answer as a letter.

Example

If $A = 2$, $B = 5$, $C = 9$, $D = 14$ and $E = 21$, what is the value of: $B + C = ?$ <u>D</u>

If $A = 6$, $B = 3$, $C = 10$, $D = 24$ and $E = 7$, what is the value of:

53. $A \times B + A$ = _____

54. $D - C + E \div B$ = _____

If A = 17, B = 6, C = 25, D = 3 and E = 7, what is the value of:

55. A + C ÷ E = _____

56. C + E + D − A ÷ B = _____

If A = 3, B = 7, C = 14, D = 21 and E = 5 , what is the value of:

57. D ÷ A + B = _____

58. C + D ÷ E = _____

/6

Write these words into each grid so that they can be read across and down the grid.

Example

STEPS   NEEDS   LAPSE   PLAIN   APPLE   POLES

P	O	L	E	S
L		A		T
A	P	P	L	E
I		S		P
N	E	E	D	S

59. HOSES   SIDES   RATED   MARSH   KITES   MAKES

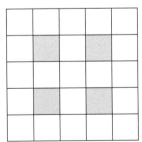

60. HOUSE   OLDEN   NEEDS   DOUSE   REEDS   OTHER

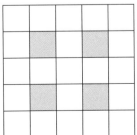

/2

/60

PAPER 17

In each of these sentences, there is a four-letter word hidden across two words. The letters are in the right order and make a correctly spelt word. Write the word.

Example

It was fis**h and** chips for supper.   _hand_

1. They went for a run twice a week. _____

2. The day was warm but windy. _____

3. The puppies lapped up the milk very quickly. _____

4. They decided to go altogether. _____

5. The old ladies had coffee there every week. _____

6. Why should we leave so long a gap? _____

/6

Write these words into each grid so that they can be read across and down the grid.

Example

AYE   YET   NET   MEN   MAY   EYE

M	E	N
A	Y	E
Y	E	T

7. YOU   AYE   HUE   ASH   EYE   SOY

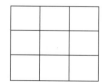

8. YET   NET   MAY   AYE   MEN   EYE

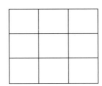

/2

In each sentence below, the word in capitals has three letters missing. The missing letters make a correctly spelt three-letter word. Write the three-letter word.

Example

CABE and beans were her favourite vegetables.   _BAG_

9. The sudden noise gave her a FHT. _____

10. Everyone was recommending this new THPY. _____

11. The old man was rushed into HOSAL. _____

12. The weekly MET was always busy. _____

13. They went skiing every TER. _____

/6

14. The GAR was unable to fix the car. _____

Move one letter from the first word and add it to the second word to make two new, correctly spelt words. The order of the letters **cannot** be changed.

Example

hunt   pit ➔ _hut_   _pint_

15. rally   heat   ➔   _____   _____

16. cinder   metal   ➔   _____   _____

17. chimp   aid   ➔   _____   _____

18. meander   horse   ➔   _____   _____

19. float   vet   ➔   _____   _____

20. pulp   bending   →   _____   _____

21. feather story   →   _____   _____

22. faster   rat   →   _____   _____

/8

Look carefully at these letter sequences. Work out the pattern to find the missing letters. Write them on the answer line. The alphabet is here to help you.

A B C D E F G H I J K L M N O P Q R S T U V W X Y Z

Example

AB   DE   GH   JK   ?   <u>MN</u>

23. VZ   GE   UY   CA   _____   YW

24. LU   JV   HW   _____   DY

25. MN   OQ   RU   _____   AF

26. NA   OZ   MC   PX   _____   QV

27. ZC   AF   BI   CL   _____

28. PD   SE   TH   _____   XL

/6

Choose two words, one from each set of brackets, so that the second pair of words is completed in the same way as the first pair. Underline the words.

Example

Solid is to (gas, lump, <u>liquid</u>) as ice is to (<u>water</u>, cube, fridge).

29. Rocks is to (geology, fossil, stone) as plants is to (garden, leaves, botany).

30. On is to (switch, up, off) as heads is to (luck, tails, choice).

31. Tea is to (leaf, cup, pot) as wine is to (red, white, glass).

32. Beginner is to (expert, novice, child) as learner is to (apprentice, lesson, new).

33. Wood is to (saw, hammer, fire) as meat is to (dinner, steak, knife).

34. Arm is to (head, shoulder, limb) as finger is to (digit, ring, thumb).

35. Pentagon is to (five, polygon, shape) as pyramid is to (Egypt, polyhedron, maths).

36. Beginning is to (start, end, cover) as source is to (water, mouth, geography).

/6

> Which of the following words **cannot** be made from the letters of the word written in capitals?

Example

STATIONERY   state   stone   <u>towns</u>   notes   train

37. PLEASANT   please   staple   plant   slant   pleat

38. WINTERY   wine   twin   wry   town   tyre

39. TELESCOPE   pelt   pole   cope   coat   steel

40. FOUNTAIN   faint   noun   often   font   faun

41. TRIUMPH   thump   trip   rump   hurt   tripe

42. HARMONY   moan   harm   maroon   roan   many

/6

> In each group of five words below, there are three words that go together in some way. Identify the two words that **do not** belong to the group and underline them.

Example

cow   horse   <u>snake</u>   cat   <u>fly</u>

43. stone   cliff   rock   boulder   gorge

44. contemporary   present   past   current   dated

45. individual   crowd   gang   crew   couple

46. coupons   ration   allocation   sample   share

47. money   purse   currency   wallet   cash

48. rich   poor   wealthy   prosperous   famous

49. whales   dolphins   elephants   sharks   eels

50. spectacle   display   shower   exhibit   glasses

/8

Look carefully at the codes and work out the answers to the questions.

Example

If the code for READ is * < @ #, what is the code for EAR ?   < @ *

If the code for DELAYED is @ # > * < # @:

51. What is the code for DEAD? _____

52. What does the code @ * > # stand for? _____

53. What is the code for LADLE? _____

If the code for MANAGER is *acdcuet:*

54. What is the code for RANGE? _____

55. What does the code *uteed* stand for? _____

56. What is the code for GARAGE? _____

57. What does the code *tcdu* stand for? _____

/7

Substitute the values for the letters and work out these equations. Give each answer as a letter.

Example

If A = 2, B = 5, C = 9, D = 14 and E = 21, what is the value of:

B + C = ?   D

If A = 8, B = 3, C = 9, D = 2 and E = 11, what is the value of:

58. C ÷ B + A = _____

/3

59. A + B + E ÷ D = _____

60. E + C − A − B = _____

/60

PAPER 18

Write these words into each grid so that they can be read across and down the grid.

Example

AYE   YET   NET   MEN   MAY   EYE

1. TEN   AWE   PAT   OWE   POD   DEN

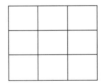

2. TOP   NET   ODE   IDE   TIN   PET

/2

Which two words are the most similar in meaning? Underline one word from each set of brackets.

Example

(run, <u>slide</u>, swing)   (<u>slip</u>, skip, jump)

3. (approximate, devise, specific)   (precise, inaccurate, monitor)

4. (bonfire, tip, rubble)   (scaffolding, debris, clearance)

5. (preside, prestige, powerful)   (statue, status, pontificate)

6. (stone, chisel, sculpture)   (carving, artistic, wood)

7. (cape, anorak, scarf)   (mantle, blanket, monocle)

8. (tunnel, pipe, dike)   (canal, marsh, ditch)

9. (placard, magazine, signpost)   (strike, hoarding, advertisement)

10. (vision, modern, design)   (architect, map, plan)

/8

In each sentence below, the word in capitals has three letters missing. The missing letters make a correctly spelt three-letter word. Write the three-letter word.

Example

CABE and beans were her favourite vegetables.   _BAG_

11. The old SERT looked after the rich lady. _____

12. The bright SLET dress was her favourite colour! _____

13. They were rescued from the EMKMENT. _____

14. The box was full of local PUCE. _____

15. They had an excellent lunch in the CANN. _____

16. It was late when the PY finished. _____

/6

Look carefully at these letter sequences. Work out the pattern to find the missing letters. Write them on the answer line. The alphabet is here to help you.

A B C D E F G H I J K L M N O P Q R S T U V W X Y Z

Example

AB   DE   GH   JK   ?   _MN_

17. QN   RL   SJ   TH   _____

18. MK   RF   WA   _____   GQ

19. SZ   RY   PW   _____   IP

20. TA   VE   XI   ZM   _____

21. FW   LT   RQ   _____   DK

22. GI   RN   FH   SO   EG   _____

23. AD   BF   CF   DH   EH   _____

24. XM   WL   UJ   TI   _____

/8

Move one letter from the first word and add it to the second word to make two new, correctly spelt words. The order of the letters **cannot** be changed.

Example

hunt   pit   ➔   hut   pint

25. petal   tiling   ➔   _____   _____

26. crane   sauce   ➔   _____   _____

27. choke   allow   ➔   _____   _____

28. glass   win   ➔   _____   _____

29. flatten   wit   ➔   _____   _____

30. whines   self   ➔   _____   _____

31. clover   panting   ➔   _____   _____

32. weaves   laden   ➔   _____   _____

/8

In each of these sentences, there is a four-letter word hidden across two words. The letters are in the right order and make a correctly spelt word. Write the word.

Example

It was fis**h and** chips for supper.   hand

33. The debris kept falling from the rafters.   _____

34. It was time to get the roof fixed.   _____

35. She was sent all the way back again.   _____

36. He must ice the cake for her birthday.   _____

37. We must ban knives from public places. _____

38. They had a picnic one day. _____

> In each group of five words below, there are three words that go together in some way. Identify the two words that **do not** belong to the group and underline them.

Example

cow   horse   <u>snake</u>   cat   <u>fly</u>

39. climate   rain   hail   sun   snow

40. forest   prairie   orchard   plain   copse

41. comedian   giggle   joke   chuckle   laugh

42. bicycle   wheelbarrow   tricycle   motorbike scooter

43. box   plastic   chest   cardboard container

44. hutch   trough   sty   stable   gate

45. peril   danger   accident   hazard   safety

46. emergency   hurricane   crisis   tornado   typhoon

> Change the first word into the last word, by changing one letter at a time. Each new word formed has to be a proper word, correctly spelt.

Example

SWAN   <u>swam</u>   <u>swim</u>   SLIM

47. POST   _____   _____   PANE

48. CART   _____   _____   MORE

49. NEST   _____   _____   WANT

50. PANE   _____   _____   LAMP

51. WISE _____ _____ CASH

52. LINE _____ _____ PUNK

/6

Rearrange the capital letters to form a correctly spelt word that will complete each sentence sensibly. Write the word on the answer line.

Example

She led the horse to the ABTESL.   STABLE

53. The children ate too much CATHOLECO cake at the party! _____

54. Get all the PSAEEART ingredients ready first. _____

55. They took the dogs for a long walk in the YCRUOTN. _____

56. She set off, determined to complete the ISONSMI. _____

57. They were totally lost in the fog without a PSCMAOS. _____

58. They could see snow on the distant INOMUTASN. _____

59. The old grey GOAAONRK had a very strong tail. _____

60. The children's band even had a BOTNMORE player. _____

/8

/60

Progress grid

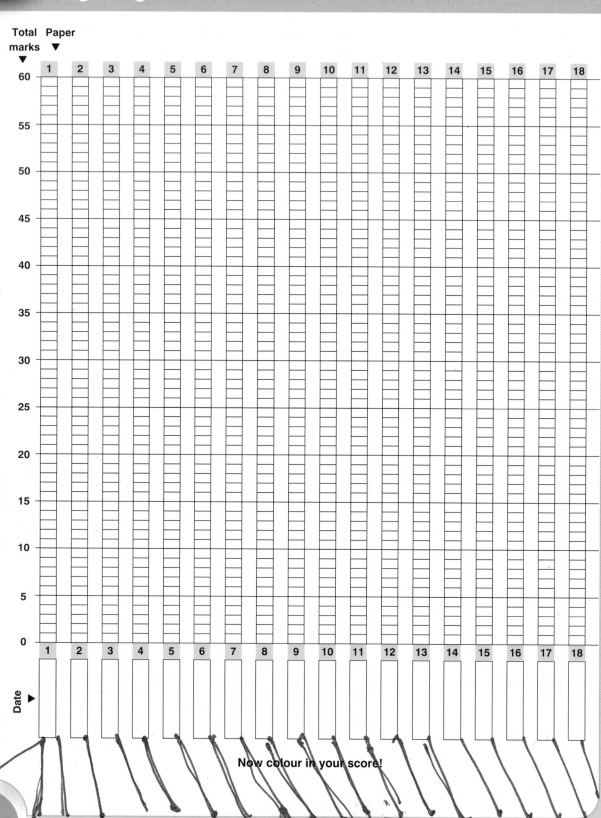

Total marks ▼   **Paper** ▼

| 1 | 2 | 3 | 4 | 5 | 6 | 7 | 8 | 9 | 10 | 11 | 12 | 13 | 14 | 15 | 16 | 17 | 18 |

60
55
50
45
40
35
30
25
20
15
10
5
0

| 1 | 2 | 3 | 4 | 5 | 6 | 7 | 8 | 9 | 10 | 11 | 12 | 13 | 14 | 15 | 16 | 17 | 18 |

Date ▶

Now colour in your score!